A-Level Year 2
Physics

Exam Board: OCR A

Revising for Physics exams is stressful, that's for sure — even just getting your notes sorted out can leave you needing a lie down. But help is at hand...

This brilliant CGP book explains **everything you'll need to learn** (and nothing you won't), all in a straightforward style that's easy to get your head around. We've also included **exam questions** to test how ready you are for the real thing.

There's even a free Online Edition you can read on your computer or tablet!

How to get your free Online Edition

Go to **cgpbooks.co.uk/extras** and enter this code...

1313 8578 8469 5969

This code only works for one person. If somebody else has used this book before you, they might have already claimed the Online Edition.

A-Level revision? It has to be CGP!

Published by CGP

Editors:
Emily Garrett, Simon Little, David Maliphant, Rachael Marshall, Sam Pilgrim, Frances Rooney, Charlotte Whiteley,
Sarah Williams and Jonathan Wray

Contributors:
Peter Cecil, Mark Edwards, Barbara Mascetti, John Myers, Zoe Nye, Moira Steven, Andy Williams

ISBN: 978 1 78294 344 0

Clipart from Corel®
Printed by Elanders Ltd, Newcastle upon Tyne.

Based on the classic CGP style created by Richard Parsons.

Contents

The Scientific Process

'How Science Works' is all about the scientific process — how we develop and test scientific ideas. It's what scientists do all day, every day (well, except at coffee time — never come between a scientist and their coffee).

Scientists Come Up with **Theories** — Then **Test Them**...

Science tries to explain **how** and **why** things happen — it **answers questions**. It's all about seeking and gaining **knowledge** about the world around us. Scientists do this by **asking** questions, **suggesting** answers and then **testing** their suggestions to see if they're correct — this is the **scientific process**.

1) **Ask** a question about **why** something happens or **how** something works. E.g. why are distant galaxies moving away from us?

2) **Suggest** an answer, or part of an answer, by forming a **theory** (a possible **explanation** of the observations) — e.g. because the universe began with a hot big bang, and has been expanding ever since. (Scientists also sometimes form a **model** too — a **simplified picture** of what's physically going on.)

3) Make a **prediction** or **hypothesis** — a **specific testable statement**, based on the theory, about what will happen in a test situation. For example, if the universe began with a hot big bang, we should still be able to see the electromagnetic radiation produced in the early stages of the universe.

4) Carry out a **test** — to provide **evidence** that will support the prediction (or help to disprove it). E.g. sending satellites to investigate the cosmic microwave background radiation (p.37).

According to James and Archie's theory of cyclical fashion, it was only a matter of time before their look was back on top.

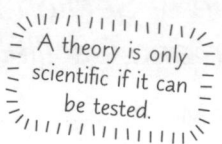

A theory is only scientific if it can be tested.

...Then They **Tell** Everyone About Their **Results**...

The results are **published** — scientists need to let others know about their work. Scientists publish their results in **scientific journals**. These are just like normal magazines, only they contain **scientific reports** (called papers) instead of the latest celebrity gossip.

1) Scientific reports are similar to the **lab write-ups** you do in school. And just as a lab write-up is **reviewed** (marked) by your teacher, reports in scientific journals undergo **peer review** before they're published.

2) The report is sent out to **peers** — other scientists that are experts in the **same area**. They examine the data and results, and if they think that the conclusion is reasonable it's **published**. This makes sure that work published in scientific journals is of a **good standard**.

3) But peer review **can't guarantee** the science is **correct** — other scientists still need to **reproduce** it.

4) Sometimes **mistakes** are made and bad work is published. Peer review **isn't perfect** but it's probably the best way for scientists to self-regulate their work and to publish **quality reports**.

...Then **Other Scientists** Will **Test** the Theory Too

Other scientists read the published theories and results, and try to **test the theory** themselves. This involves:

- Repeating the **exact same experiments**.
- Using the theory to make **new predictions** and then testing them with **new experiments**.

If the **Evidence** Supports a Theory, It's **Accepted** — for Now

1) If all the experiments in all the world provide good evidence to back it up, the theory is thought of as **scientific 'fact'** (for now).

2) But it will never become **totally indisputable** fact. Scientific **breakthroughs or advances** could provide new ways to question and test the theory, which could lead to **new evidence** that **conflicts** with the current evidence. Then the testing starts all over again...

And this, my friend, is the **tentative nature of scientific knowledge** — it's always **changing** and **evolving**.

The Scientific Process

So scientists need evidence to back up their theories. They get it by carrying out experiments, and when that's not possible they carry out studies. But why bother with science at all? We want to know as much as possible so we can use it to try and improve our lives (and because we're nosy).

Evidence Comes From Controlled Lab Experiments...

1) Results from **controlled experiments** in **laboratories** are **great**.
2) A lab is the easiest place to **control variables** so that they're all **kept constant** (except for the one you're investigating).

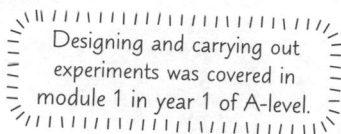
Designing and carrying out experiments was covered in module 1 in year 1 of A-level.

...That You can Draw Meaningful Conclusions From

1) You always need to make your experiments as **controlled** as possible so you can be confident that any effects you see are linked to the variable you're changing.
2) If you do find a relationship, you need to be careful what you conclude. You need to decide whether the effect you're seeing is **caused** by changing a variable (this is known as a **causal relationship**), or whether the two are just **correlated**. Drawing conclusions was covered in module 1 in year 1 of A-level.

Andy had concluded that there was a causal relationship between growing a beard and popularity with seals.

Society Makes Decisions Based on Scientific Evidence

1) Lots of scientific work eventually leads to **important discoveries** or breakthroughs that could **benefit humankind**.
2) These results are **used by society** (that's you, me and everyone else) to **make decisions** about the way we live, what we eat, what we drive, etc.
3) All sections of society use scientific evidence to make decisions, e.g. politicians use it to devise policies and individuals use science to make decisions about their own lives.

Other factors can **influence** decisions about science or the way science is used:

Economic factors

Society has to consider the **cost** of implementing changes based on scientific conclusions — e.g. the cost of reducing the UK's carbon emissions to limit the human contribution to **global warming**. Scientific research is often **expensive**. E.g. in areas such as astronomy, the Government has to **justify** spending money on a new telescope rather than pumping money into, say, the **NHS** or **schools**.

Social factors

Decisions affect **people's lives** — e.g. when looking for a site to build a **nuclear power station**, you need to consider how it would affect the lives of the people in the **surrounding area**.

Environmental factors

Many scientists suggest that building **wind farms** would be a **cheap** and **environmentally friendly** way to generate electricity in the future. But some people think that because **wind turbines** can **harm wildlife** such as birds and bats, other methods of generating electricity should be used.

So there you have it — how science works...

Hopefully these pages have given you a nice intro to how science works, e.g. what scientists do to provide you with 'facts'. You need to understand this, as you're expected to know how science works yourself — for the exam and for life.

Phases of Matter and Temperature

You need energy to heat something up, and to change its state. Everything comes down to energy. Pretty much always.

The **Three Phases of Matter** are Defined by the **Arrangement of Particles**

You'll remember these **three phases** (or states) **of matter** (**solid**, **liquid** and **gas**) from GCSE — but here's a quick recap just in case.

Solids

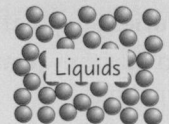

Liquids

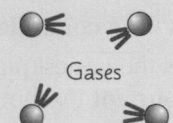

Gases

| Particles vibrate about fixed positions in a regular lattice. They're held in position by strong forces of attraction. | Particles are constantly moving around and are free to move past one another, but are attracted to each other. | Particles are free to move around with constant random motion. There are no forces of attraction between particles in an ideal gas. |

The idea that solids, liquids and gases are made up of **tiny** moving or vibrating **particles** is called the **kinetic model of matter**. It seems obvious now, but this **wasn't** always accepted by the scientific community. It took **several scientists** and **hundreds of years** to **develop** a **controversial idea** into an **accepted theory**.

Brownian Motion Supports Kinetic Theory

1) In 1827, botanist Robert Brown noticed that tiny particles of pollen suspended in water moved with a **zigzag**, **random motion**. This type of movement is known as **Brownian motion**.

2) You can **observe** Brownian motion in the lab:
   - Put some **smoke** in a **brightly illuminated** glass jar and observe the particles using a **microscope**.
   - The smoke particles appear as **bright specks** moving **haphazardly** from side to side, and up and down.

3) Brown couldn't explain this, but nearly 80 years later Einstein showed that this provided evidence for the existence of atoms or **molecules** in the air (the kinetic model of matter). The **randomly moving** air particles were hitting the smoke particles unevenly, causing this motion.

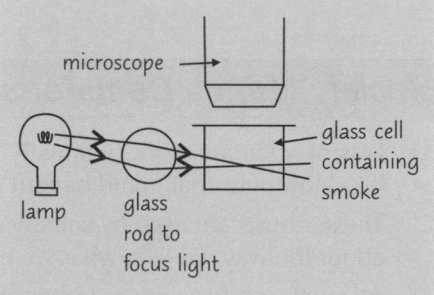

microscope

glass cell containing smoke

lamp   glass rod to focus light

Internal Energy is the Sum of Kinetic and Potential Energy

1) All things (solids, liquids, gases) have **energy** contained within them. The amount of **energy** contained in a system is called its **internal energy** — it's found by **summing** the **kinetic** and **potential** energies of all the **particles** within it.

> **Internal energy** is the **sum** of the **kinetic** and **potential energy** of the **particles** within a system.

2) The **kinetic energy** of a particle depends on its **mass** and **speed**. Through **kinetic theory**, the average kinetic energy is proportional to **temperature** — the **hotter** the temperature, the **higher** the **average kinetic energy**.

3) **Potential energy** is caused by **interactions** between particles and is based on their **positions** relative to each other.

4) These energies are **randomly distributed** amongst the particles.

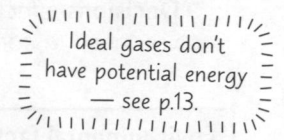

Ideal gases don't have potential energy — see p.13.

A **Change of Phase** Means a **Change of Internal Energy**

1) When you **heat** a substance, you **increase** its **temperature** — thereby **increasing** the **kinetic energy** of the particles within it and its **internal energy**.

2) When a substance **changes phase**, its **internal energy** changes, but its **kinetic energy** (and temperature) **doesn't**. This is because the change of phase is altering the bonds and therefore **potential energy** of the particles.

3) For example, in a pan of **boiling water**, the **potential energy** of the water molecules **increases** as they break free of the liquid. But the water in both phases is at **100 °C**.

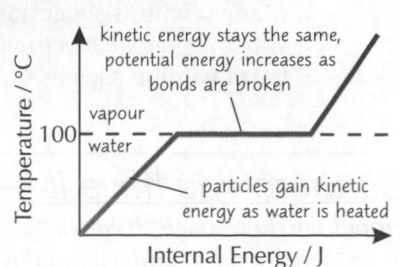

kinetic energy stays the same, potential energy increases as bonds are broken

vapour

water

100

particles gain kinetic energy as water is heated

Internal Energy / J

Phases of Matter and Temperature

There's an *Absolute Scale* of *Temperature*

The **Celsius scale** uses the **freezing** and **boiling points** of **water** (0 °C and 100 °C) to make a temperature scale which can be easily used for **day to day** activities. However, scientists use the **kelvin** scale (**the absolute scale of temperature**) for **all equations** in **thermal physics**.

It's also known as the **thermodynamic scale**, and it does not **depend** on the properties of any **particular substance**, unlike the **Celsius** scale.

Zero kelvins is the **lowest possible temperature** and is called **absolute zero***.

At **0 K** all particles have the **minimum** possible **internal energy** — everything theoretically stops — at higher temperatures, particles have more energy. In fact, with the **Kelvin scale**, a particle's **energy** is **proportional** to its **temperature** (see page 13).

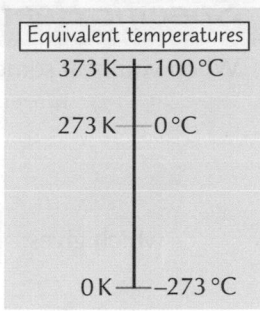
Equivalent temperatures
373 K — 100 °C
273 K — 0 °C
0 K — −273 °C

1) The Kelvin scale is named after Lord Kelvin who first suggested it.

2) A change of **1 K** equals a change of **1 °C**.

3) To change from degrees Celsius into kelvins you **add 273** (or subtract 273 to go the other way).

$$T(\text{K}) \approx \theta(^\circ\text{C}) + 273$$

*It's true. −273 °C is the lowest temperature theoretically possible. Weird, huh. You'd kinda think there wouldn't be a minimum, but there is.

If *A* and *B* are in *Thermal Equilibrium* with *C, A* is in *Equilibrium* with *B*

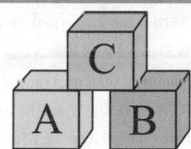

If **body A** and **body B** are both in **thermal equilibrium** with **body C**, then **body A** and **body B** must be in thermal equilibrium with **each other**.

1) Suppose A, B and C are three identical metal blocks. A has been in a **warm oven**, B has come from a **refrigerator** and C is at **room temperature**.

2) **Thermal energy** flows from A to C and C to B until they all reach **thermal equilibrium** and the net flow of energy stops. This happens when the three blocks are at the **same temperature**.

Thermal energy is **always** transferred from regions of **higher temperature** to regions of **lower temperature**.

Practice Questions

Q1 What is internal energy?

Q2 What happens to the kinetic and potential energies of water molecules as water boils?

Q3 Explain the difference between the Celsius and Kelvin scales.

Q4 What is the boiling point of water in kelvins?

Q5 State in degrees Celsius the lowest possible temperature that a substance could theoretically be cooled to and explain why it cannot be cooled any further.

Q6 Describe what will happen to the thermal energy and temperatures of a hot metal tray and a cold metal spoon when they are placed touching each other.

Exam Questions

Q1 Describe the spacing, ordering and motion of particles in solids, liquids and gases. [3 marks]

Q2 Brownian motion provides evidence for the continual random motion of particles in a gas.

a) Describe an experiment you could use to demonstrate Brownian motion. [2 marks]

b) Explain how Brownian motion supports the theory of the random movement of particles. [2 marks]

Browniean motion — we collided, then I dropped the cake down the stairs...

Celsius, I'm sorry — it's not you it's me, I just need someone more absolute and proportional, who is always positive. We'll still be friends and see each other in weather forecasts and ovens, we just can't be together in thermal physics...

Thermal Properties of Materials

This couple of pages has more heat than Guy Fawkes on bonfire night. Phwoar...

Specific Heat Capacity is how much Energy it Takes to Heat Something

When you heat something, the amount of energy needed to raise its **temperature** depends on its **specific heat capacity**.

> The **specific heat capacity** (*c*) of a substance is the amount of **energy** needed to **raise** the **temperature** of **1 kg** of the substance by **1 K** (or 1°C).

which gives:

> **energy change = mass × specific heat capacity × change in temperature**

in symbols: $E = mc\Delta\theta$ ⟵ *Q* is sometimes used instead of *E* for the change in thermal energy.

E is the energy change in J, *m* is the mass in kg and $\Delta\theta$ is the temperature change in K or °C.
Units of *c* are $J\,kg^{-1}\,K^{-1}$ or $J\,kg^{-1}\,°C^{-1}$.

You can Measure Specific Heat Capacity in the Laboratory

The **method** is the same for **solids** and **liquids**, but the **set-up** is a little bit different:

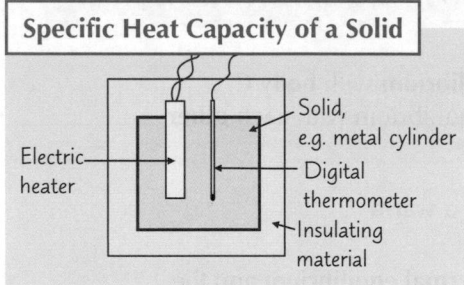

Specific Heat Capacity of a Solid

Electric heater — Solid, e.g. metal cylinder — Digital thermometer — Insulating material

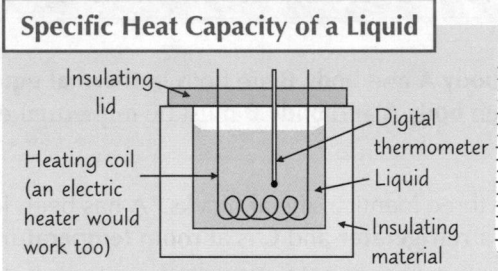

Specific Heat Capacity of a Liquid

Insulating lid — Heating coil (an electric heater would work too) — Digital thermometer — Liquid — Insulating material

The value you end up with for c will probably be too high by quite a long way. That's because some of the energy from the heater gets transferred to the air and the container. If you're really keen, start below and finish above room temperature to cancel out gains and losses.

Method for both experiments:

1) **Heat** the substance with the heater. You need a **temperature rise** of about 10 K to get an **accurate** value of *c*.

2) With an ammeter and voltmeter attached to your **electric heater** you can work out the energy supplied. Calculate the energy (*E*) using: $E = W = VIt$ (*V* is the heater voltage, *I* is the current and *t* is the time in seconds)

3) Plug your data into: $E = mc\Delta\theta$ to calculate *c*.

> **Example:** You heat 0.250 kg of water from 12.1 °C to 22.9 °C with an electric immersion heater. The heater has a voltage of 11.2 V and a current of 5.30 A, and is switched on for 205 s. Calculate the specific heat capacity of water.
>
> $E = VIt = 11.2 \times 5.30 \times 205 = 12\,168.8$ J $\qquad \Delta\theta = 22.9 - 12.1 = 10.8$ °C
>
> $E = mc\Delta\theta$ so $c = \dfrac{E}{m\Delta\theta} = \dfrac{12\,168.8}{0.250 \times 10.8} = 4506.9... = \mathbf{4510\ J\,kg^{-1}\,°C^{-1}}$ (or 4510 $J\,kg^{-1}\,K^{-1}$) **(to 3 s.f.)**

Estimating the Specific Heat Capacity of a Metal Block Using the Method of Mixtures

1) Heat a metal block of known mass, m_b, up to a temperature T_b.

2) Quickly transfer this block into a container containing a mass of water, m_w, at a temperature T_w.

3) The hot block will heat the water. Measure the temperature of the water once it has reached a **steady** value, T_s.

4) The **heat (energy) gained** by the water is **equal** to the **heat lost** by the block, so:

$m_w c_w \Delta\theta_w = m_b c_b \Delta\theta_b$ which becomes: $m_w c_w (T_s - T_w) = m_b c_b (T_b - T_s)$

5) Rearrange for c_b: $c_b = \dfrac{m_w c_w (T_s - T_w)}{m_b (T_b - T_s)}$

Thermal Properties of Materials

Specific Latent Heat is the Energy Required to Change State per kg

To **melt** a **solid**, you need to **break the bonds** that hold the particles in place. The **energy** needed for this is called the **latent heat of fusion**. Similarly, when you **boil or evaporate a liquid**, **energy is needed** to **pull the particles apart** completely. This is the **latent heat of vaporisation**.

The **larger** the **mass** of the substance, the **more energy** it takes to **change** its **state**. That's why the **specific latent heat** is defined per kg:

> The **specific latent heat** (**L**) of **fusion** or **vaporisation** is the quantity of **thermal energy** required to **change the state** of **1 kg** of a substance.

You wouldn't be laughing if it was your bum stuck to the ice. I need some latent heat energy, pronto.

which gives:

> **energy change = mass of substance changed × specific latent heat**

or in symbols:

> $E = mL$

You'll usually see the latent heat of vaporisation written L_v and the latent heat of fusion written L_f

Where **E** is the energy change in J and **m** is the mass in kg. The units of **L** are J kg^{-1}.

Measuring the Specific Latent Heat of a Solid or Liquid

For a **solid**, e.g. ice:

1) Put a **heating coil** and equal masses of ice in **two funnels** above **beakers**.

2) Turn on **one** heating coil for **three minutes**. Record the **energy transferred** in the three minutes. **Don't** turn on the other coil — it's there so you can measure how much ice **melts** due to the **ambient temperature** of the room.

3) At the end of the three minutes, **measure** the **mass of water** collected in the beakers. Subtract one from the other to get the mass of ice, m, that melted **solely** due to the presence of the **heater**.

4) $E = mL$, so to find the **specific latent heat of fusion** for water just **divide** the energy supplied by the mass of ice that melted: $L = E \div m$

For a **liquid**, you can do a very similar experiment — **boil** water in a **distilling flask**, **condense** the **vapour** given off and divide the energy transferred by the mass of condensed water collected.

Practice Questions

Q1 Define specific heat capacity.

Q2 Show that the thermal energy needed to heat 2 kg of water from 20 °C to 50 °C is ~250 kJ (c_{water} = 4180 Jkg^{-1}K^{-1}).

Q3 Describe an experiment to determine the specific heat capacity of olive oil.

Q4 Describe two ways you could measure the specific heat capacity of a metal block.

Q5 Define the specific latent heats of fusion and vaporisation and describe experiments to find them for water.

Exam Questions

Q1 A 2.0 kg metal cylinder is heated uniformly from 4.5 °C to 12.7 °C in 3.0 minutes. The electric heater supplies energy at a rate of 90.0 Js^{-1}. Assuming that heat losses are negligible, calculate the specific heat capacity of the metal. State a correct unit for your answer. [3 marks]

Q2 A 4.0 kg metal block is heated to 100 °C (correct to 2 significant figures). It is then transferred into a container holding 2.0 kg of water (c = 4180 J kg^{-1} K^{-1}) at a temperature of 19 °C. The water warms to a steady temperature of 26 °C. Find an estimate for the specific heat capacity of the metal. [2 marks]

Q3 A 3.00 kW electric kettle contains 0.500 kg of water already at its boiling point. Neglecting heat losses, calculate the length of time it will take to boil dry. (L_v (water) = 2.26 × 10^6 J kg^{-1}) [3 marks]

My specific eat capacity — 24 pies...

This stuff's a bit dull, but hey... make sure you're comfortable using those equations. Interesting(ish) fact for the day — the huge difference in specific heat capacity between the land and the sea is one of the causes of monsoons in Asia.

Ideal Gases

Aaahh... great... another one of those 'our equation doesn't work properly with real gases, so we'll invent an ideal gas that it does work for and they'll think we're dead clever' situations. Hmm. Physicists, eh...

There are **Three Gas Laws...**

> A (theoretical) **ideal gas** obeys all three gas laws

The three gas laws were each worked out **independently** by **careful experiment**. Each law applies to a **fixed mass** of gas.

Boyle's Law: pV = constant

At a **constant temperature**, the **pressure** p and **volume** V of a gas are **inversely proportional**.

The higher the temperature of the gas, the further the curve is from the origin.

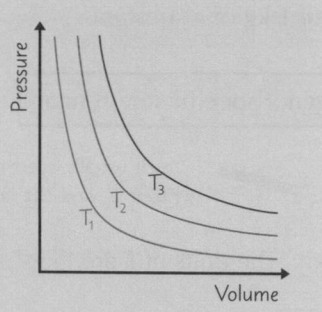

The Pressure Law: $p \div T$ = constant

At a constant **volume**, the **pressure** p of a gas is **directly proportional** to its **absolute temperature** T.

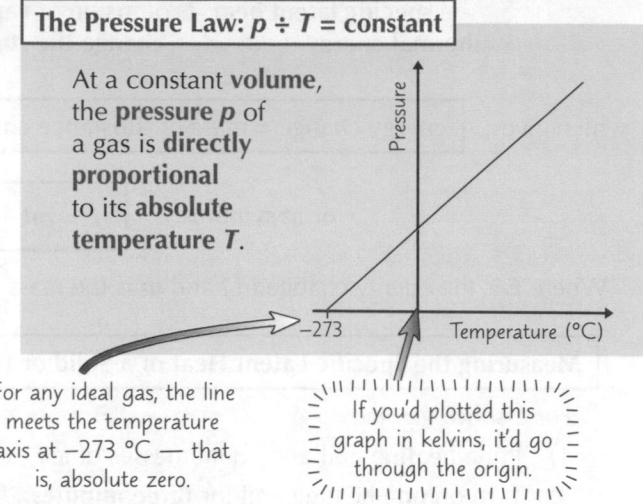

For any ideal gas, the line meets the temperature axis at −273 °C — that is, absolute zero.

If you'd plotted this graph in kelvins, it'd go through the origin.

The third gas law, **Charles's Law**, says that at a constant **pressure**, the **volume** V of a gas is **directly proportional** to its **absolute temperature** T.

...which you can **Demonstrate** with these **Experiments**

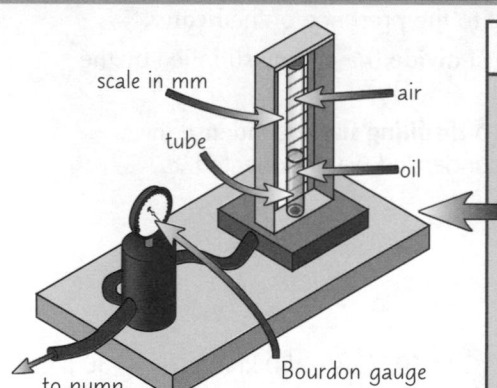

scale in mm
air
tube
oil
to pump
Bourdon gauge

Experiment to investigate pressure and volume (Boyle's Law)

1) You can investigate the effect of **pressure** on **volume** by setting up the experiment shown. The **oil** confines a parcel of air in a sealed **tube** with **fixed dimensions**. A **tyre pump** is used to **increase** the pressure in the tube and the **Bourdon gauge** records the **pressure**. As the pressure increases the air will **compress** and the volume occupied by air in the tube will **reduce**.

2) Measure the volume of air when the system is at **atmospheric pressure**, then gradually increase the pressure noting down **both** the pressure and the volume of air. Multiplying them together at any point should give a **constant**.

Experiment to estimate absolute zero (Pressure Law)

1) Immerse a stoppered flask of **air** in a beaker of water so that as much as possible of the flask is **submerged**. Connect the stopper to a **Bourdon gauge** using a short length of tube — the volume of the tubing must be **much smaller** than the volume of the flask. Record the **temperature** of the water and the **pressure** on the gauge.

2) **Heat** the water for a few minutes then remove the heat, **stir** the water to ensure it is at a **uniform temperature** and allow some time for the heat to be **transferred** from the water to the air. Record the **pressure** on the gauge and the **temperature**, then heat the water again and **repeat** until the water boils.

3) **Repeat** your experiment **twice** more with **fresh cool water**.

4) Plot your results on a graph of **pressure** against **temperature**. Draw a **line of best fit**. Estimate the value of **absolute zero** by continuing (extrapolating) your line of best fit until it crosses the *x*-axis.

If the markings on your measuring equipment are quite far apart, you can often interpolate between them (e.g. if the temperature is halfway between the markings for 24 °C and 25 °C you could record it as 24.5 °C). But it's better to use something with a finer scale if you can.

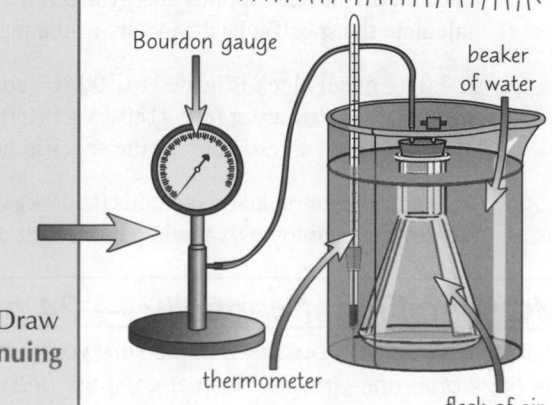

Bourdon gauge
beaker of water
thermometer
flask of air

MODULE 5: SECTION 1 — THERMAL PHYSICS

Ideal Gases

If you **Combine** All Three you get the **Equation of State**

Combining all three gas laws gives the equation: $p\frac{V}{T} = \text{constant}$

1) The constant in the equation depends on the amount of gas used. The amount of **gas** can be **measured** in moles, **n**.

2) The constant then becomes **nR**, where **R** is called the **molar gas constant**. Its value is 8.31 J mol^{-1} K^{-1}. Plugging this into the equation gives:

$p\frac{V}{T} = nR$ or rearranging, $pV = nRT$ — **the equation of state of an ideal gas**

> p is pressure (Pa),
> V is volume (m^3),
> T is temperature (K),
> n is amount of gas in moles (see below)

3) This equation works well (i.e., real gases approximate to an ideal gas) for gases at **low pressures** and fairly **high temperatures**.

The **Boltzmann Constant** k is like a **Gas Constant** for **One Particle** of Gas

One mole of **any** material contains the same **number of particles**, no matter what the material is. This number is called **Avogadro's constant** and has the symbol N_A. The value of N_A is **6.02 × 10^{23} particles per mole**.

1) The **number of particles**, N, in an amount of gas is given by the **number of moles**, n, multiplied by **Avogadro's constant**, N_A.

$N = nN_A$

2) The **Boltzmann constant**, k, is given by $k = \frac{R}{N_A}$ — you can think of the Boltzmann constant as the **gas constant** for **one particle of gas**, while R is the gas constant for **one mole of gas**.

3) The value of the Boltzmann constant is **1.38 × 10^{-23} JK^{-1}**.

4) If you combine $N = nN_A$ and $k = R/N_A$ you'll see that $Nk = nR$ — which can be substituted into the equation of state to give this alternative form (in terms of number of particles N, rather than moles, n).

$pV = NkT$

Practice Questions

Q1 State Boyle's Law and describe an experiment you could use to investigate it.

Q2 Describe an experiment you could use to find an estimate for the value of absolute zero.

Q3 The pressure of a gas is 100 000 Pa and its temperature is 27.0 °C. The gas is heated — its volume stays fixed but the pressure rises to 150 000 Pa. Show that its new temperature is 177 °C.

Q4 Give the equation of state of an ideal gas and use the Boltzmann constant to derive an alternative form.

Exam Questions

Q1 The pressure inside a gas cylinder is 1.04 × 10^6 Pa at 10.0 °C. It is heated in a fire to 62.3 °C. Calculate the new pressure inside the cylinder. [2 marks]

Q2 The mass of one mole of nitrogen gas is 0.0280 kg. $R = 8.31$ J mol^{-1} K^{-1}.
   a) A flask contains 0.0140 kg of nitrogen gas.
      i) Calculate the number of moles of nitrogen gas in the flask. [1 mark]
      ii) Calculate the number of nitrogen molecules in the flask. [1 mark]

   b) The flask has a volume of 0.0100 m^3 and is at a temperature of 27.0 °C. Calculate the pressure inside. [2 marks]

   c) Describe the effect on the pressure if the number of molecules of nitrogen in the flask was halved. [1 mark]

Q3 A large helium balloon has a volume of 10.0 m^3 at ground level. The temperature of the gas in the balloon is 293 K and the pressure is 1.00 × 10^5 Pa. The balloon is released and rises to a height where its volume becomes 25.0 m^3 and its temperature is 261 K. Calculate the pressure inside the balloon at its new height. [3 marks]

Ideal revision equation: marks = (pages read × questions answered)²...

All this might sound a bit theoretical, but most gases you'll meet in the everyday world come fairly close to being 'ideal'. They only stop obeying these laws when the pressure's too high or they're getting close to their condensing point.

The Pressure of an Ideal Gas

Kinetic theory tries to explain the gas laws. It basically models a gas as a series of hard balls that obey Newton's laws.

You Can Use Newton's Laws to **Explain** the **Pressure** of an **Ideal Gas**

Imagine a cubic box containing *N* particles of an ideal gas, each with a mass *m*.

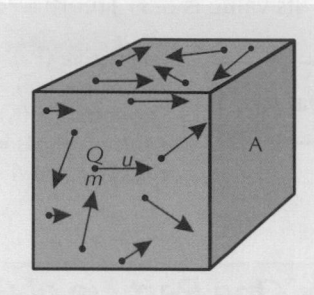

1) The particles of the gas are **free to move** around with **constant random motion**. There are **no forces of attraction** between the particles, so according to **Newton's 1st law**, they continue to move with **constant velocity** until they collide with another particle or the box itself.

2) When a particle **collides** with a **wall** of the box, it exerts a **force** on the wall, and the wall exerts an **equal and opposite force** on the particle. This is **Newton's 3rd law** in action.

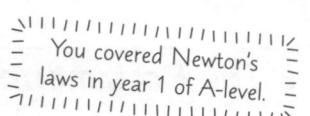
You covered Newton's laws in year 1 of A-level.

3) The **size of the force** exerted by the particle on the wall can be **calculated** using **Newton's 2nd law**, which says the **force is equal to the rate of change of momentum**.

4) For example, if particle **Q** is travelling directly towards wall **A** with velocity **u**, its momentum is **mu**. When it **hits** the wall, the force of the **impact** causes it to rebound in the **opposite direction**, at the same speed. Its **momentum** is now **–mu**, which means the **change in momentum** is 2**mu**.

5) So, the **force** a particle exerts is **proportional** to its **mass** and its **velocity**. The **mass** of a single **gas particle** is **tiny** (for example, an atom of helium gas is only 6.6×10^{-27} kg), so each particle can only exert a **minuscule force**.

6) But, there **isn't** just **one particle** in the box — there's probably **millions of billions** of them. The **combined force** from so many tiny particles is **much bigger** than the contribution from any individual particle.

Imagine putting a single grain of sugar into a lunchbox and shaking it around — the box might as well be empty. Now put a couple of spoonfuls of sugar in, and shake that around — this time you'll hear the sugar thumping against the walls of the box as it collides. You don't notice the effect of the individual grains, only the combined action of loads of them.

7) Because there are so many particles in the box, a **significant number** will be **colliding** with each wall of the box at **any given moment**. And because the particles' motion is **random**, the **collisions** will be **spread** all over the surface of each wall. The result is a **steady**, **even force** on all the walls of the box — this is **pressure**.

Pressure is **Proportional** to the **Number of Particles**, their **Mass** and **Speed**

So, the pressure in a gas is a result of all the **collisions** between particles and the **walls** of the container. Using a method similar to that above you can obtain this equation for the pressure of an ideal gas:

$$pV = \frac{1}{3}Nm\overline{c^2}$$

$\overline{c^2}$ is the mean square speed — it represents the mean of the squared speeds of all the particles.

The equation shows that the pressure exerted by a gas depends on **four** things:

1) The **volume**, *V*, of the container — increasing the volume of the container decreases the **frequency of collisions** because the particles have **further to travel** in between collisions. This decreases the pressure.

2) The **number of particles**, *N* — increasing the number of particles increases the **frequency of collisions** between the particles and the container, so increases the **total force** exerted by all the collisions.

3) The **mass**, *m*, of the particles — according to Newton's 2nd law, **force is proportional to mass**, so **heavier** particles will exert a **greater force**.

4) The **speed**, *c*, of the particles — the **faster** the particles are going when they hit the walls, the **greater** the **change in momentum** and **force** exerted.

The Pressure of an Ideal Gas

Lots of **Simplifying Assumptions** are Used in **Kinetic Theory**

In **kinetic theory**, physicists picture gas particles moving at **high speed** in **random directions**.
To get relations like the one on the previous page, some **simplifying assumptions** are needed:

1) The gas contains a **large number of particles**.
2) The particles **move rapidly** and **randomly**.
3) The **volume** of the **particles** is **negligible** when compared to the volume of the **gas**.
4) **Collisions** between particles themselves or between particles and the walls of the container are **perfectly elastic**.
5) The duration of each collision is **negligible** when compared to the time **between collisions**.
6) There are **no forces** between particles except for the moment when they are in a collision.

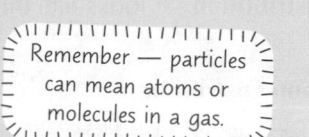
Remember — particles can mean atoms or molecules in a gas.

Don't make an ass of yourself — learn the assumptions.

A **gas obeying** these **assumptions** is called an **ideal** gas. Real gases behave like ideal gases as long as the **pressure isn't too big** and the **temperature** is **reasonably high** (compared with their boiling points).

The **Root Mean Square Speed** or **c**$_{rms}$ is a **Useful Quantity**

As you saw on the previous page, it often helps to think about the motion of a **typical particle** in kinetic theory.

1) c^2 is the **mean square speed** and has **units m²s⁻²**.
2) $\overline{c^2}$ is the average of the **squared speeds** of **all** the particles, so the square root of it gives you the typical speed.
3) This is called the **root mean square speed** or, usually, the **r.m.s. speed**. It's often written as c_{rms}. The **unit** is the same as any speed — **ms⁻¹**.

$$c_{rms} = \sqrt{\text{mean square speed}} = \sqrt{\overline{c^2}}$$

Practice Questions

Q1 Describe how Newton's laws can be used to explain the pressure in an ideal gas.

Q2 Write down the equation linking pressure of an ideal gas with the mean square speed of the gas particles.

Q3 List the assumptions made about ideal gas behaviour.

Q4 What is the 'mean square speed'? What are its units?

Exam Questions

Q1 Describe and explain the factors that influence the pressure exerted by a gas. [4 marks]

Q2 Some helium gas is contained in a flask of volume 7.00×10^{-5} m³.
Each helium atom has a mass of 6.65×10^{-27} kg, and there are 2.17×10^{22} atoms present.
The pressure of the gas is 1.03×10^5 Pa.

a) Calculate the mean square speed of the atoms. [2 marks]

b) Calculate the r.m.s. speed of a typical helium atom in the flask. [1 mark]

So that's mean square speed, next up: cantankerous hexagon velocity...

Crikey, if that's kinetic theory after a load of simplifying assumptions I'd hate to see the uncensored version. Speaking of assumptions, if you can't name all six of them right now you'd better go back and learn the lot pronto. Go on, just see if you can write them down. Yes, now. I'm watching you. Don't believe me? Nice... er... jumper...

Internal Energy of an Ideal Gas

Particles in gases all have different amounts of kinetic energy, and it all depends on the absolute temperature...

Molecules in a Gas *Don't* all have the *Same Amount of Energy*

Imagine looking down on **Oxford Street** when it's teeming with people. You'll see some people ambling along **slowly**, some hurrying **quickly**, but most of them will be walking with a **moderate speed**.

It's the same with the **molecules** in a gas. Some **don't have much kinetic energy** and move **slowly**. Others have **loads of kinetic energy** and **whizz** along. But most molecules are somewhere **in between**.

If you plot a **graph** of the **numbers of molecules** in a gas with different **kinetic energies** you get a **Maxwell-Boltzmann distribution**. It looks like this:

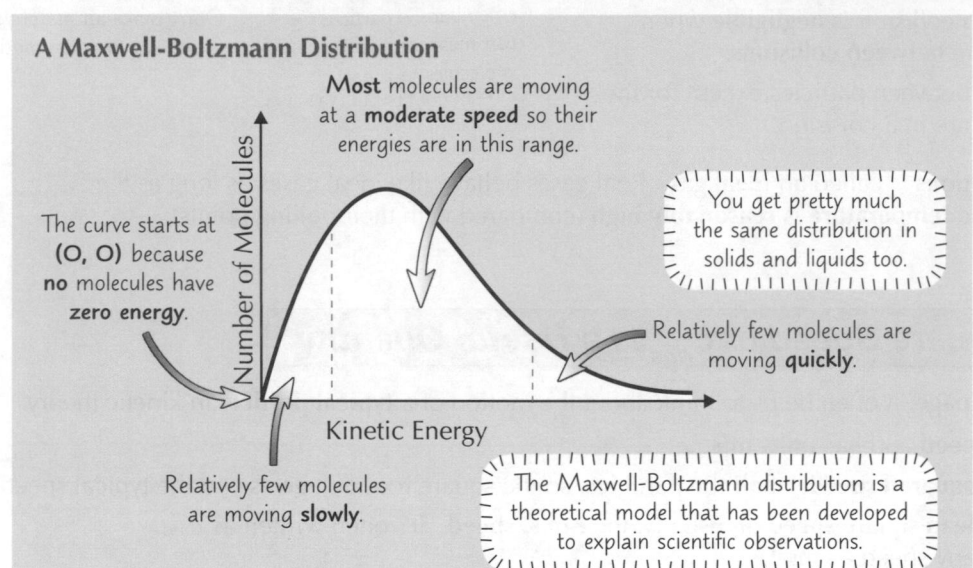

A Maxwell-Boltzmann Distribution

Most molecules are moving at a **moderate speed** so their energies are in this range.

The curve starts at (O, O) because **no** molecules have **zero energy**.

You get pretty much the same distribution in solids and liquids too.

Relatively few molecules are moving **quickly**.

Relatively few molecules are moving **slowly**.

The Maxwell-Boltzmann distribution is a theoretical model that has been developed to explain scientific observations.

Number of Molecules (y-axis)

Kinetic Energy (x-axis)

Nave's energy levels on a Monday morning are always towards the lower end of the distribution.

The *Speed Distribution* of *Gas Particles* Depends on *Temperature*

The shape of the **speed distribution** depends on the **temperature** of the gas.

Both the curves on the right represent the **same number of particles**, but the cooler curve has a higher, steeper peak at a lower speed.

As the temperature of the gas increases:
1) the **average** particle speed increases.
2) the **maximum** particle speed increases.
3) the distribution curve becomes more **spread out**.

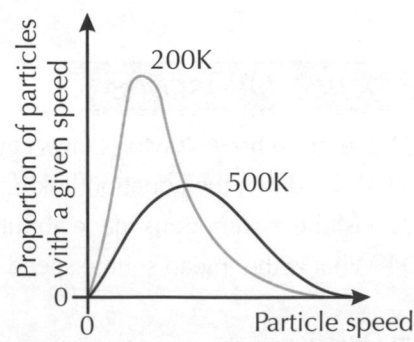

Proportion of particles with a given speed (y-axis)

200K

500K

Particle speed (x-axis)

Energy Changes Happen Between Particles

The particles of a gas **collide** with each other **all the time**. Some of these collisions will be '**head-on**' (particles moving in **opposite directions**) while others will be '**shunts from behind**' (particles moving in the **same direction**).

1) As a result of the collisions, **energy** will be **transferred** between particles.
2) Some particles will **gain speed** in a collision and others will **slow down**.
3) **Between collisions**, the particles will travel at **constant speed**.
4) Although the energy of an individual particle changes at each collision, the collisions **don't alter** the **total energy** of the **system**.
5) So, the **average** speed of the particles will stay the same provided the **temperature** of the gas **stays the same**.

Internal Energy of an Ideal Gas

Average Kinetic Energy is Proportional to Absolute Temperature

If you've been paying attention to this section, you'll know that $pV = NkT$ (from page 9) and that $pV = \frac{1}{3}Nm\overline{c^2}$ (page 10). You can **combine** these to **derive** the **kinetic energy** of gas particles.

1) $pV = NkT$

2) The **pressure** of an **ideal gas** given by kinetic theory is $pV = \frac{1}{3}Nm\overline{c^2}$

   $\overline{c^2}$ = mean square speed of particles
   N = number of particles in the gas
   m = mass of one particle
   T = absolute temperature
   $k = 1.38 \times 10^{-23}$ JK^{-1} (Boltzmann const.)

3) **Equating** these two gives: $\frac{1}{3}Nm\overline{c^2} = NkT$

4) And you can **cancel** N to give: $\frac{1}{3}m\overline{c^2} = kT$
   which you can rearrange to give $m\overline{c^2} = 3kT$

5) $\frac{1}{2}m\overline{c^2}$ is the **average kinetic energy** of an **individual particle**. (Remember $\overline{c^2}$ is a measure of speed squared, so this is just like the equation for kinetic energy, $KE = \frac{1}{2}mv^2$, that you'll know already.)

6) So multiplying both sides by $\frac{1}{2}$ gives you $\frac{1}{2}m\overline{c^2} = \frac{3}{2}kT$

7) So the **average kinetic energy, E,** of **one gas particle** is given by: 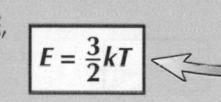 $E = \frac{3}{2}kT$

   The kinetic energy of gas particles is always an average value because the particles are all travelling at different speeds.

8) Now for a **bonus equation** — multiplying by the number of gas particles, N, gives you an equation for the **internal energy, U,** of an ideal gas: $U = \frac{3}{2}NkT$

   In an ideal gas the potential energy is 0 J because there are no forces between the particles. This means that the internal energy is equal to the total random kinetic energy only (see p4).

The equations above show that **average kinetic energy** and **internal energy** are both directly proportional to the **absolute temperature** — a **rise** in **absolute temperature** will cause an **increase** in the kinetic energy of the particles, meaning a rise in **internal energy**.

Practice Questions

Q1 Sketch a graph of a Maxwell-Boltzmann distribution and label the key characteristics.

Q2 Describe the changes in the distribution of gas particle speeds as the temperature of a gas increases.

Q3 Show how $pV = NkT$ and the equation for the pressure of an ideal gas can be combined to derive an equation for the average kinetic energy of particles in an ideal gas.

Q4 What happens to the average kinetic energy of a particle if the temperature of a gas doubles?

Exam Questions

Q1 A flask contains one mole of nitrogen at 300 K (correct to three significant figures).

   a) State the number of molecules of nitrogen in the flask. [1 mark]

   b) Calculate the average kinetic energy of a nitrogen molecule in the flask. [2 marks]

   c) Explain why all the nitrogen molecules in the flask will not have the same kinetic energy. [1 mark]

Q2 A container of neon gas is heated from 300 K to 500 K (correct to three significant figures). There are 3.00×10^{23} neon molecules in the container. ($k = 1.38 \times 10^{-23}$ JK^{-1})

   a) Calculate the change in the internal energy of the gas. [2 marks]

   b) After heating, the pressure inside the container is 1.66×10^4 Pa. Calculate the volume of the container. [2 marks]

I wish I could distribute all my energy to the weekend...

*Just to clarify — I said "**imagine**" Oxford Street. This isn't one of those practicals you need to know for the exam so no, you can't have a day out shopping while "revising physics". Unfortunately, you have to spend your time learning the derivation above — you could be tested on it. Then make sure you can use it to explain changes in kinetic energy.*

Circular Motion

*It's probably worth putting a bookmark in here — this stuff is needed **all over** the place.*

Angles can be Expressed in Radians

1) The angle in **radians**, θ, is defined as the **arc-length** divided by the radius of the circle.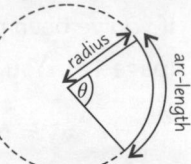

2) For a **complete circle** (360°), the arc-length is just the circumference of the circle ($2\pi r$). Dividing this by the radius (r) gives 2π. So there are 2π radians in a complete circle.

Moving between degrees and radians is pretty easy — you just need to remember this handy formula: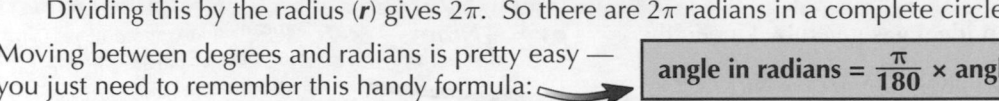

$$\text{angle in radians} = \tfrac{\pi}{180} \times \text{angle in degrees}$$

The **Angular Velocity** is the **Angle** an Object Rotates Through **per Second**

1) Just as **linear velocity**, v, is defined as displacement ÷ time, the **angular velocity**, ω, is defined as **angle ÷ time**. The unit of angular velocity is rad s⁻¹ — radians per second.

$$\omega = \frac{\theta}{t}$$

ω = angular velocity (rad s⁻¹) — the symbol for angular velocity is the little Greek 'omega', not a w. θ = angle (radians) turned through in a time, t (seconds).

Angular velocity is a vector quantity. It has a size and a direction.

2) The **linear velocity**, v, and **angular velocity**, ω, of a rotating object are linked by the equation:

$$v = r\omega$$

v = linear velocity (ms⁻¹), r = radius of the circle (m), ω = angular velocity (rad s⁻¹)

Circular Motion has a **Frequency** and **Period**

1) The **frequency**, f, is the number of complete **revolutions per second** (rev s⁻¹ or hertz, Hz).

2) The **period**, T, is the **time taken** for a complete revolution (in seconds). Frequency and period are **linked** by the equation:

$$f = \frac{1}{T}$$

f = frequency in rev s⁻¹, T = period in s

3) For a complete circle, an object turns through 2π radians in a time T, so frequency and period are related to ω by:

$$\omega = \frac{2\pi}{T} \quad \text{and} \quad \omega = 2\pi f$$

ω = angular velocity in rad s⁻¹

Objects Travelling in Circles are **Accelerating** since their **Velocity is Changing**

1) Even if the car shown on the right is going at a **constant speed**, its **velocity** is changing since its **direction** is changing.

2) Since acceleration is defined as the **rate of change of velocity**, the car is accelerating even though it isn't going any faster.

3) This acceleration is called the **centripetal acceleration** and is always directed towards the **centre of the circle**.

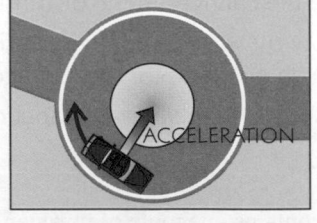

There are two formulas for centripetal acceleration:

$$a = \frac{v^2}{r} \quad \text{and} \quad a = \omega^2 r$$

a = centripetal acceleration in ms⁻², v = linear velocity in ms⁻¹, ω = angular velocity in rad s⁻¹, r = radius in m

The **Centripetal Acceleration** is produced by a **Centripetal Force**

From Newton's 1st law (which you met in year 1 of A-level), if an object has an **acceleration**, there must be a **net force** acting on it. An object will travel in a circular path if there is a constant net force acting on it perpendicular to its velocity. This is called a **centripetal force** and it **always acts towards the centre of the circle**. Since $F = ma$ (Newton's 2nd law), the centripetal force is:

$$F = \frac{mv^2}{r} \quad \text{and} \quad F = m\omega^2 r$$

The centripetal force is what keeps the object moving in a circle — remove the force and the object would fly off at a tangent.

Although the force changes the **direction** of the motion, the object's **velocity remains perpendicular** to the direction of the force. The object **never moves towards or away from** the centre of the circle, so there is no motion in the direction of the force. Hence **no work is done** on the object, and the object's **kinetic energy** (and therefore **speed**) remains **constant**.

Circular Motion

You Can **Investigate** Circular Motion With a **Whirling Bung**

1) You'll need a **rubber bung**, some **washers**, some **string** and a **glass tube**. Measure the **mass** of the bung (m_b) and the mass of the washers (m_w), then attach the bung to the string. Thread the string through the glass tube, and weigh down the free end using the washers.

2) Make a **reference mark** on the string, then measure the **distance** from the mark to the centre of the bung. Pull the string taut to make sure this measurement is as accurate as possible.

3) Line the mark up with the top of the glass tube, then begin to **spin** the bung in a **horizontal circle**, as shown in the diagram on the right. You'll need to spin it at the right speed to **keep the reference mark level** with the top of the glass tube (spin too quickly and it'll move outwards, too slowly and it'll move down). Try to keep your hand as **still as possible** whist you spin.

4) Measure the **time taken** for the bung to make **one complete circle**. This is the **time period**, **T**. In practice, this may be too small to time accurately, so you might need to measure the time taken to complete ten circles and divide to get an average.

5) You can then use the formula $\omega = \frac{2\pi}{T}$ to find the **angular velocity** of the bung, and $F = m_b\omega^2 r$ to find the **centripetal force**. In this equation, r is the radius of the circle, which should be the distance from the reference mark on the string to the centre of the bung.

6) The centripetal force should be equal to the **weight of the washers** ($W = m_w g$). This weight is what causes the tension in the string, which acts as the centripetal force.

7) Repeat this experiment for different distances between the bung and the reference mark — you should find that as r gets bigger, the **time period gets longer** but the **centripetal force stays the same**.

Make sure that the bung and the washers are securely fastened to the string, that you're not standing too close to anyone and that there's nothing breakable nearby. And remember to wear safety goggles.

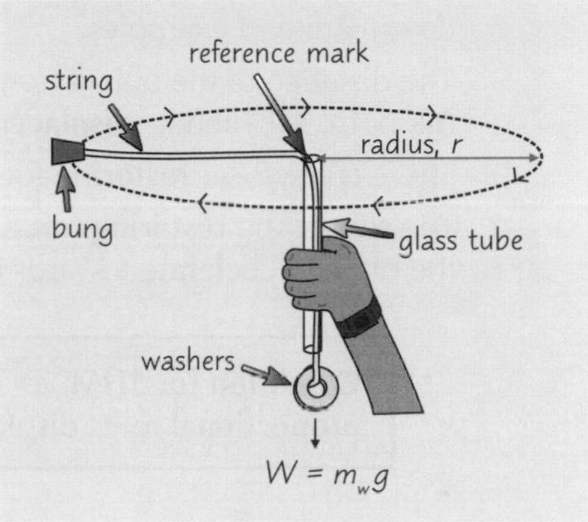

reference mark
string
radius, *r*
bung
glass tube
washers
$W = m_w g$

Stopping the string from slipping is a bit of an art, so you may need a lot of repeats.

Practice Questions

Q1 How many radians are there in a complete circle?

Q2 How is angular velocity defined? What is the relationship between angular velocity and linear velocity?

Q3 Define the period and frequency of circular motion. State the relationship between period and angular velocity.

Q4 Write down two formulas for centripetal acceleration, a, in terms of radius, r, for an object with circular motion.

Q5 In which direction does the centripetal force act, and what happens when this force is removed?

Q6 Describe an experiment to investigate the relationship between radius and time period for an object moving in a circle.

Exam Questions

Q1 a) The Earth takes 3.2×10^7 s to orbit the Sun. Assuming its orbit is a perfect circle, calculate the Earth's angular and linear velocity (the distance from the Earth to the Sun is approximately 1.5×10^{11} m). [2 marks]

   b) Given that the mass of the Earth is 6.0×10^{24} kg, calculate the centripetal force needed to keep the Earth in its orbit. State the cause of this force. [2 marks]

Q2 A bucket full of water, tied to a rope, is being swung around in a vertical circle (so it is upside down at the top of the swing). The radius of the circle is 1 m.

   a) By considering the acceleration due to gravity at the top of the swing ($g = 9.81$ ms^{-2}), what is the minimum frequency with which the bucket can be swung without any water falling out? [3 marks]

   b) The bucket is now swung with a constant angular speed of 5 rad s^{-1}. What will be the tension in the rope when the bucket is at the top of the swing if the total mass of the bucket and water is 10 kg? [2 marks]

My head is spinning after all that...

"Centripetal" just means "centre-seeking". The centripetal force is what actually causes circular motion. What you feel when you're spinning, though, is the reaction (centrifugal) force. Don't get the two mixed up.

Simple Harmonic Motion

Something simple at last — I like the sound of this. And colourful graphs too — you're in for a treat here.

SHM is Defined in Terms of *Acceleration* and *Displacement*

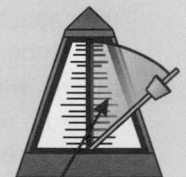

Midpoint

Small displacement, therefore small force.

Large displacement, therefore large force.

1) An object moving with **simple harmonic motion** (SHM) **oscillates** to and fro, either side of a **midpoint**. **Pendulums** and **mass-spring systems** (e.g. a mass hanging on a spring that's free to move up and down) are two examples.

2) The distance of the object from the midpoint is called its **displacement**.

3) There is always a **restoring force** pulling or pushing the object back **towards** the **midpoint**.

4) The **size** of the **restoring force** depends on the **displacement**, and the force makes the object **accelerate** towards the midpoint.

> **Condition for SHM**: an oscillation in which the **acceleration** of an object is **directly proportional** to its **displacement** from the **midpoint**, and is directed **towards the midpoint**.

The *Restoring Force* Makes the Object Exchange *PE* and *KE*

1) The **type** of **potential energy** (*PE*) depends on **what it is** that's providing the **restoring force** — e.g. **gravitational *PE*** for pendulums or **elastic *PE*** (elastic stored energy) for masses on springs moving horizontally.

2) As the object moves **towards the midpoint**, the restoring force **does work** on the object and so **transfers** some *PE* to *KE*. When the object is moving **away from the midpoint**, the object's *KE* is transferred **back to** *PE* again.

3) As the object passes the **midpoint**, its *PE* is **zero** and its *KE* is **maximum**.

4) At the **maximum displacement** (the **amplitude**) on both sides of the midpoint, the object's *KE* is **zero** and its *PE* is at its **maximum**.

5) The **sum** of the **potential** and **kinetic** energy is called the **mechanical energy** and **stays constant** (as long as the motion isn't damped — see p.20-21).

6) The **energy transfer** for one complete cycle of oscillation is: *PE* to *KE* to *PE* to *KE* to *PE*... and then the process repeats...

Energy

$E_p + E_k$

E_p

E_k

left-hand side   right-hand side   Displacement

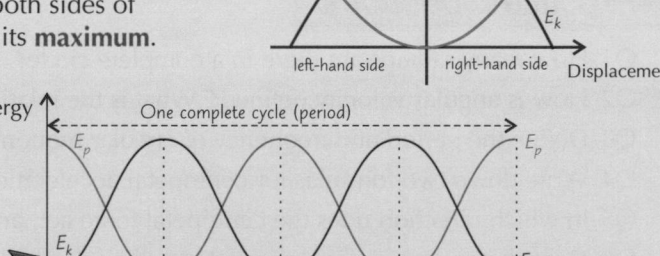

Energy

One complete cycle (period)

E_p E_p

E_k E_k

Time

Left   Midpoint   Right   Midpoint   Left

You can Draw *Graphs* to Show *Displacement*, *Velocity* and *Acceleration*

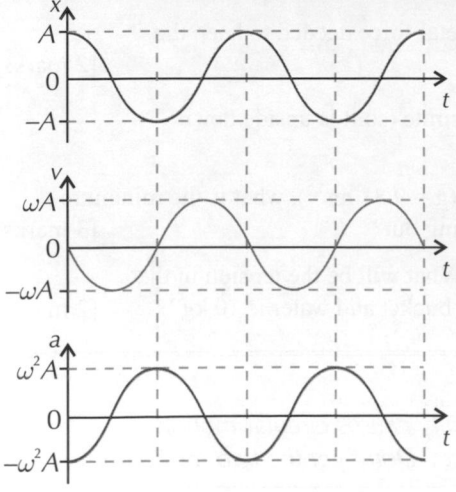

Displacement, *x*, varies with time, *t*, as a cosine (or sine) wave with a maximum value, **A** (the amplitude).

Velocity, *v*, is the gradient of the **displacement-time** graph. It is a **quarter of a cycle** in front of the **displacement** (a phase difference of $\pi/2$) and has a maximum value of *ωA*.

Acceleration, *a*, is the gradient of the **velocity-time** graph. It has a maximum value of $\omega^2 A$, and is in **antiphase** with the **displacement**.

ω is the **angular frequency** of the oscillation (in rad s^{-1}). It is the **magnitude** of the vector quantity angular velocity:

$$\omega = 2\pi f \quad \text{and} \quad \omega = \frac{2\pi}{T}$$

Where *T* is the time taken for one oscillation and *f* is the number of oscillations per second (see next page).

Simple Harmonic Motion

The *Frequency* and *Period* Don't Depend on the *Amplitude*

1) From **maximum positive displacement** (e.g. maximum displacement to the right) to **maximum negative displacement** (e.g. maximum displacement to the left) and **back again** is called a **cycle** of oscillation.

2) The **frequency**, *f*, of the SHM is the **number of cycles per second** (measured in Hz).

3) The **period**, *T*, is the **time** taken for a **complete cycle** (in seconds).

> In SHM, the **frequency** and **period** are independent of the **amplitude** (they're constant for a given oscillation), so a **pendulum clock** will keep ticking in **regular** time **intervals** even if its swing becomes very **small**. This kind of oscillator is called an **isochronous oscillator**.

Learn the SHM Equations

Make sure your calculator is set to radians before you use these equations.

1) According to the definition of SHM, the **acceleration**, *a*, is directly proportional to the **displacement**, *x*. The **constant of proportionality** is equal to $-\omega^2$. There's a minus sign in the equation because the acceleration is always in the **opposite direction** to the displacement.

Acceleration: $a = -\omega^2 x$ Maximum acceleration: $a_{max} = \omega^2 A$

Don't forget, A is the maximum displacement — it's not acceleration.

2) **Velocity** is a vector quantity, so the **direction** of motion matters as well as the **speed** — that's why there's a ± sign.

Velocity: $v = \pm\omega\sqrt{A^2 - x^2}$ Maximum velocity: $v_{max} = \omega A$

When $v = v_{max}$, $x = 0$

3) The **displacement** varies with time according to one of two equations, depending on **where** the object was when the timing was started. This determines whether the displacement-time graph is a cosine or sine wave.

If you began timing when the displacement was at its **maximum**: $x = A\cos(\omega t)$

If you began timing as the object passed through the **midpoint**: $x = A\sin(\omega t)$

These are solutions of the equation $a = -\omega^2 x$.

Practice Questions

Q1 Sketch a graph to show how both the kinetic and potential energy vary with displacement for an object oscillating with simple harmonic motion. Explain the shape of the graph you've drawn.

Q2 Sketch a graph of how the velocity of an object oscillating with SHM varies with time.

Q3 A mass on a spring oscillates with simple harmonic motion. A timer is started as it passes the midpoint. Write formulas for the displacement, velocity and acceleration of the mass.

Exam Questions

Q1 a) Define simple harmonic motion. [2 marks]
   b) Explain why the motion of a ball bouncing off the ground is not simple harmonic motion. [1 mark]

Q2 A pendulum is pulled 0.05 m to the left and released. It oscillates with simple harmonic motion with a frequency of 1.5 Hz. Calculate:
   a) its maximum velocity, [1 mark]
   b) its displacement 0.1 s after it is released, [1 mark]
   c) the time it takes for its displacement to fall to 0.01 m after it is released. [2 marks]

Q3 Two pendulums, X and Y, are oscillating with simple harmonic motion. Pendulum X has the same maximum displacement as pendulum Y, but twice the angular speed. Which option correctly describes the maximum acceleration of pendulum X with respect to pendulum Y?
   A half   B the same   C double   D quadruple [1 mark]

"Simple" harmonic motion — hmmm, I'm not convinced...

Don't let all the 'ω's confuse you, this stuff's actually not too bad. Make sure you can remember the shapes of all the graphs on page 16. And make sure you're comfortable with all the formulas on these pages too.

Investigating Simple Harmonic Motion

You can investigate simple harmonic motion in a few different ways — make sure you've read pages 16-17 before you tackle this lot, or it won't make much sense.

You Can Investigate Simple Harmonic Motion Using a *Data Logger*...

Data loggers and **sensors** are a great way of investigating simple harmonic motion, as they allow you to make **precise measurements**. You still need to know what you're doing though.

To investigate the simple harmonic motion of a **mass on a spring** using a data logger and a position sensor:

1) Set up the equipment as shown in the diagram (if you don't have a long spring you could connect a few shorter ones together).

2) Lift the mass slightly and release it — this will cause the mass-spring system to start **oscillating** with **simple harmonic motion**. To make sure your experiment is **repeatable**, place a ruler behind the spring to measure how far you raise the mass. Make sure your eye is **level** with the mass when you take the measurement. You should also try to lift the mass straight up, to stop the mass from swinging from side to side.

3) As the mass oscillates, the **position sensor** will measure the **displacement** of the mass over **time**. The computer can be set to record this data automatically.

4) Let the experiment run until you've got a good amount of data (at least ten complete oscillations).

5) Once you've collected your data, you can use the computer to generate a **displacement-time** graph.

6) From the graph, you can measure *T*, the **time period** of the oscillation, and *A*, the **amplitude** of the oscillation. You should find that the amplitude of the oscillations gets **smaller** over time, but the time period remains **constant**:

> *The string helps to stop the mass from swinging from side to side.*

string → Clamp and clamp stand

spring — Ruler

mass — workbench

position sensor

to computer

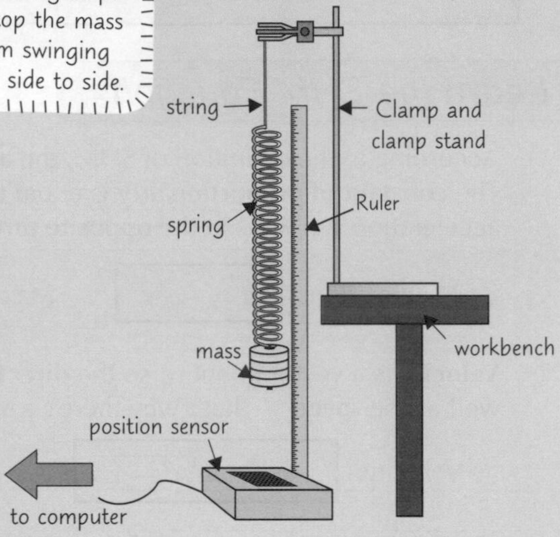

> *The longer the spring, the larger the amplitude of oscillations you can make so the lower the percentage error in your measurement.*

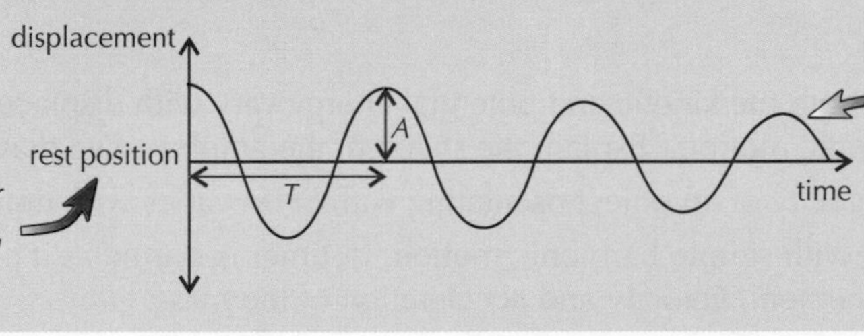

displacement

rest position

Depending on how your position sensor is set up, this may be zero.

A

T

time

If you leave the system oscillating for long enough, the amplitude will decrease until the mass eventually comes to rest. This is because energy is lost to overcoming air resistance as the mass moves up and down.

You can use this system to investigate how **different variables** affect the time period of the oscillation.

You could investigate the effect of changing:
- the **weight** of the mass,
- the **stiffness** of the spring,
- the size of the **initial displacement**.

If you're investigating the effect of changing one of these factors, you need to be careful to **control all the others**. You'll need to repeat the experiment for each value of every independent variable you investigate.

You should find:
- the **heavier** the mass, the **longer** the time period,
- the **stiffer** the spring, the **shorter** the time period,
- the **initial displacement** has **no effect** on the time period.

Sorry everyone, not that kind of spring...

Investigating Simple Harmonic Motion

... or **Without One**

If you don't have a data logger, you won't be able to generate a displacement-time graph, but you can still investigate the **time period** of an oscillation. For example, you can investigate the simple harmonic motion of a pendulum using the equipment in the diagram below and a **stopwatch**:

1) Set up the equipment as shown on the right. Measure the **weight** of the mass, and use a ruler to find the **length** of the string.

2) Move the mass to the side, keeping the string **taut**. Measure the **angle** between the string and the vertical using the protractor. Make sure it's **less than 10°**, or the mass won't swing with simple harmonic motion when you release it.

3) Release the mass. Position your eye **level with the mark on the card**, and start the stopwatch when the mass passes in front of it.

4) Record the time when the mass passes the mark again, **moving from the same direction**. This is the **time period** of the oscillator. Depending on your pendulum, T might be too short to measure accurately from one swing. If so, measure the total time for a number of complete oscillations combined (say 5 or 10) and take an average.

5) Keep recording T at regular intervals as the motion dies away. You should find that T **remains constant** as the amplitude of the swing decreases.

6) You can investigate how different factors affect the motion of the pendulum by changing the weight of the **mass** on the string, the **length** of the string, and the **angle** that you turn the string through before you first release it (still keeping it below 10°). Measure all the variables as **accurately** as possible, and only change **one variable at a time**.

7) You should find that the **angle** of the initial displacement and the **weight of the mass** have **no effect** on the time period of the pendulum, but as the **length** of the string increases the **time period increases**.

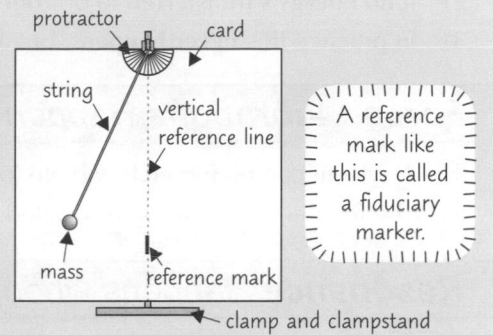

A reference mark like this is called a fiduciary marker.

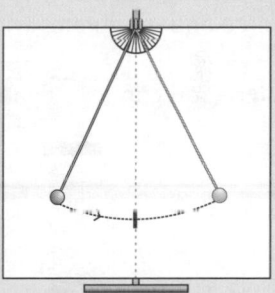

Only record the times when the mass passes in front of the mark from the same direction (e.g. from left to right), or you won't get the time period of a complete oscillation.

Your data will contain more random errors if you don't use a data logger, so you'll need to do more repeats.

Practice Questions

Q1 Give one advantage of using a data logger instead of a stopwatch to investigate simple harmonic motion.

Q2 Describe an experiment to investigate the simple harmonic motion of a mass on a spring.

Q3 What effect does increasing the weight of the mass have on:
a) the simple harmonic motion of a mass on a spring?
b) the simple harmonic motion of a mass on a pendulum?

Exam Question

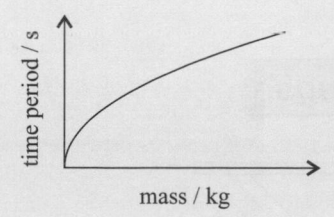

Q1 The graph on the left shows the results of an experiment to investigate how the time period of an object oscillating vertically on a spring is affected by its mass.

a) Describe how the experiment might have been conducted. [4 marks]

b) Describe the relationship shown by the graph. [2 marks]

I keep oscillating between confusion and bewilderment...

Two lovely experiments here for you to learn — make sure you understand how to swap them round, too. You can measure the time period of a spring using a stopwatch and reference mark, and you can use a data logger and a sensor to investigate the SHM of a pendulum. (You'd use an angle sensor where the protractor is instead of a position sensor.)

Free and Forced Vibrations

Resonance… tricky little beast. The Millennium Bridge was supposed to be a feat of British engineering, but it suffered from a severe case of the wobbles caused by resonance. How was it sorted out? By damping, of course — read on…

Free Vibrations — No Transfer of Energy To or From the Surroundings

1) If you stretch and release a mass on a spring, it oscillates at its **natural frequency**.

2) If **no energy's transferred** to or from the surroundings, it will **keep** oscillating with the **same amplitude forever**.

3) In practice this **never happens**, but a spring vibrating in air is called a **free vibration** (or oscillation) anyway.

Forced Vibrations Happen when there's an External Driving Force

1) A system can be **forced** to vibrate (or oscillate) by a periodic **external force**.

2) The frequency of this force is called the **driving frequency**.

Resonance Happens when Driving Frequency = Natural Frequency

When the **driving frequency** approaches the **natural frequency**, the system gains more and more energy from the driving force and so vibrates with a **rapidly increasing amplitude**. When this happens the system is **resonating**.

Example: You can investigate how amplitude varies with driving frequency using a system like the one below.

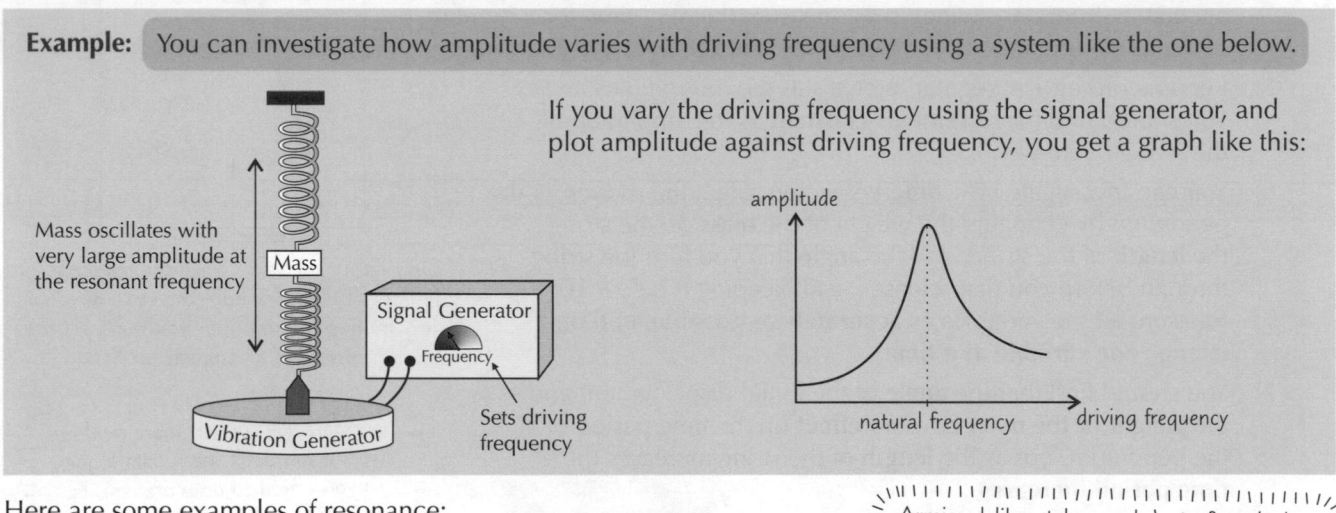

If you vary the driving frequency using the signal generator, and plot amplitude against driving frequency, you get a graph like this:

Mass oscillates with very large amplitude at the resonant frequency

Mass

Signal Generator
Frequency

Sets driving frequency

Vibration Generator

amplitude

natural frequency   driving frequency

Here are some examples of resonance:

a) organ pipe
The column of air resonates, driven by the motion of air at the base.

b) swing
A swing resonates if it's driven by someone pushing it at its natural frequency.

Armies deliberately march 'out of step' when they cross a bridge. This reduces the risk of the bridge resonating and breaking apart.

c) glass smashing
A glass resonates when driven by a sound wave of the right frequency. This can make the glass break.

d) radio
A radio is tuned so the electric circuit resonates at the same frequency as the radio station you want to listen to.

Damping Happens when Energy is Lost to the Surroundings

1) In practice, **any** oscillating system **loses energy** to its surroundings.

2) This is usually down to **frictional forces** like air resistance.

3) These are called **damping forces**.

4) Systems are often **deliberately damped** to **stop** them oscillating or to **minimise** the effect of **resonance**.

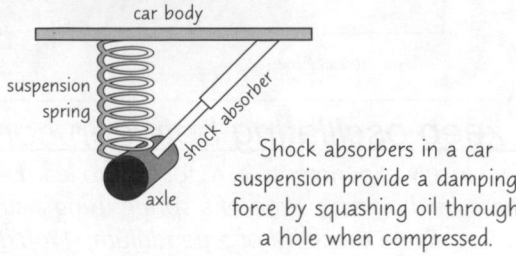

car body

suspension spring

shock absorber

axle

Shock absorbers in a car suspension provide a damping force by squashing oil through a hole when compressed.

MODULE 5: SECTION 2 — CIRCULAR MOTION AND OSCILLATIONS

Free and Forced Vibrations

Different Amounts of Damping have Different Effects

1) The **degree** of damping can vary from **light** damping (where the damping force is small) to **overdamping**.

2) Damping **reduces** the **amplitude** of the oscillation over time. The **heavier** the damping, the **quicker** the amplitude is reduced to zero.

3) **Critical damping** reduces the amplitude (i.e. stops the system oscillating) in the **shortest possible time**.

4) Car **suspension systems** and moving coil **meters** (which control the arm in analogue voltmeters and ammeters) are critically damped so that they **don't oscillate** but return to equilibrium as quickly as possible.

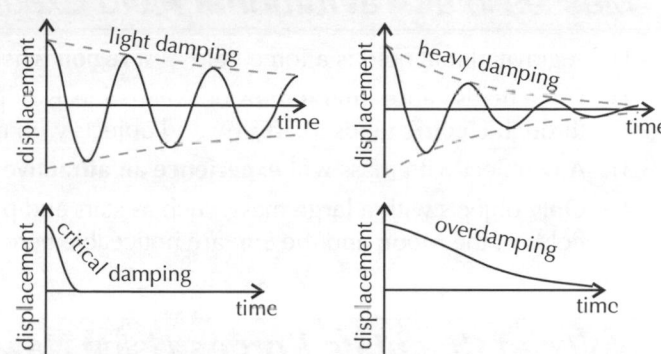

5) Systems with **even heavier damping** are **overdamped**. They take **longer** to return to equilibrium than a critically damped system.

6) **Plastic deformation** of ductile materials **reduces** the **amplitude** of oscillations in the same way as damping. As the material changes shape, it **absorbs energy**, so the oscillation will become smaller.

Damping Affects Resonance too

1) **Lightly damped** systems have a **very sharp** resonance peak. Their amplitude only increases dramatically when the **driving frequency** is **very close** to the **natural frequency**.

2) **Heavily damped** systems have a **flatter response**. Their amplitude doesn't increase very much near the natural frequency and they aren't as **sensitive** to the driving frequency.

> Structures are damped to avoid being damaged by resonance. Loudspeakers are also made to have as flat a response as possible so that they don't 'colour' the sound.

Example: You can show how damping affects resonance using the experiment on the previous page.

Here's how increasing the damping affects resonance in this system:

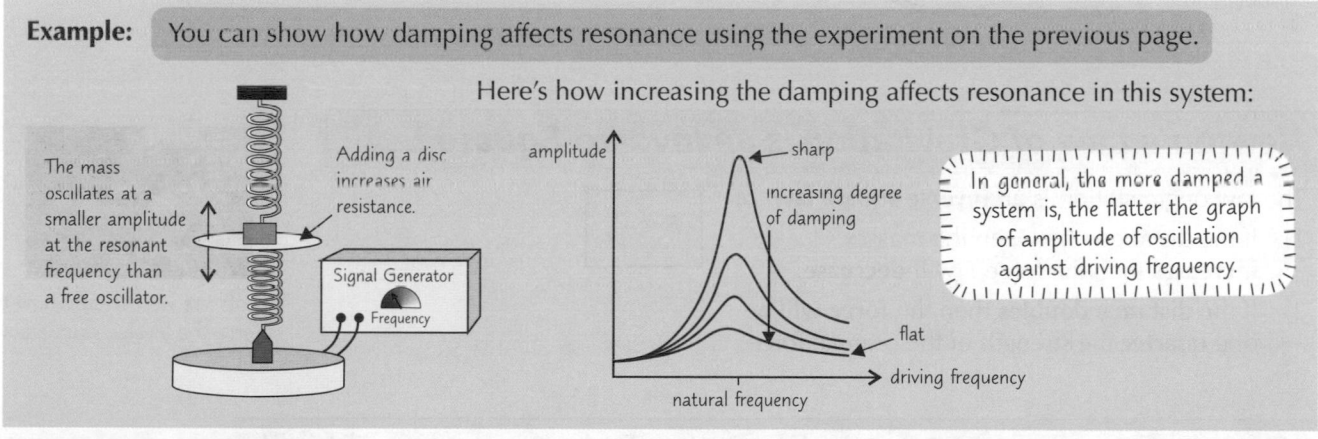

The mass oscillates at a smaller amplitude at the resonant frequency than a free oscillator.

Adding a disc increases air resistance.

Signal Generator
Frequency

sharp

increasing degree of damping

flat

> In general, the more damped a system is, the flatter the graph of amplitude of oscillation against driving frequency.

amplitude

natural frequency

driving frequency

Practice Questions

Q1 What is a free vibration? What is a forced vibration?

Q2 Give an example of resonance.

Exam Questions

Q1 a) Define resonance. [2 marks]

b) Draw a diagram to show how the amplitude of a lightly damped system varies with driving frequency. [2 marks]

c) On the same diagram, show how the amplitude of the system varies with driving frequency when it is heavily damped. [1 mark]

Q2 Define critical damping and state a situation where it is used. [2 marks]

Physics — it can really put a damper on your social life...

Resonance can be really useful (radios, organ pipes, swings — yay) or very, very bad...

Gravitational Fields

Gravity's all about masses attracting each other. If the Earth didn't have a gravitational field, apples wouldn't fall to the ground and you'd probably be floating off into space instead of sitting here reading this page...

Masses in a **Gravitational Field** Experience a **Force of Attraction**

1) A gravitational field is a force field — a **region** where an object will experience a **non-contact force**.

2) Force fields cause **interactions** between objects or particles — e.g. **static** or **moving charges** interact through **electric** fields (p. 46-49) and objects with **mass** interact through **gravitational** fields.

3) Any object with mass will **experience an attractive force** if you put it in the **gravitational field** of another object.

4) Only objects with a **large** mass, such as stars and planets, have a significant effect. E.g. the gravitational fields of the **Moon** and the **Sun** are noticeable here on Earth — they're the main cause of our **tides**.

You can **Calculate Forces** Using **Newton's Law of Gravitation**

1) The **force** experienced by an object in a gravitational field is always **attractive**. It's a **vector** which depends on the **masses** involved and the **distance** between them.

2) The diagram shows the force acting on mass *m* due to mass *M*. (The force on *M* due to *m* is equal but in the opposite direction.)

3) *M* and *m* are **uniform spheres**, which behave as **point masses** — as if all their mass is concentrated at the centre.

4) It's easy to work out the **force** experienced by a **point mass** in a **gravitational field** — you just put the numbers into this **equation**, known as **Newton's law of gravitation**:

It doesn't matter what you call the masses, M and m, m_1 and m_2, Paul and Larry...

The negative sign shows that the vector F is in the opposite direction to r (displacement of m from M).

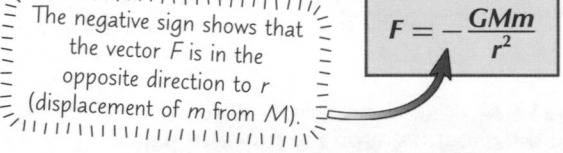

$$F = -\frac{GMm}{r^2}$$

where *F* is the force acting on mass *m* due to mass *M*, *M* and *m* behave as point masses, *G* is the gravitational constant — 6.67×10^{-11} Nm²kg⁻² and *r* is the distance (in metres) between the centres of the two masses.

Newton's Law of Gravitation is an **Inverse Square Law**

The law of gravitation is an **inverse square law** so:

1) If the distance *r* between the masses **increases** then the force *F* will **decrease**.

2) If the **distance doubles** then the **force** will be one **quarter** the strength of the original force.

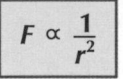

$$F \propto \frac{1}{r^2}$$

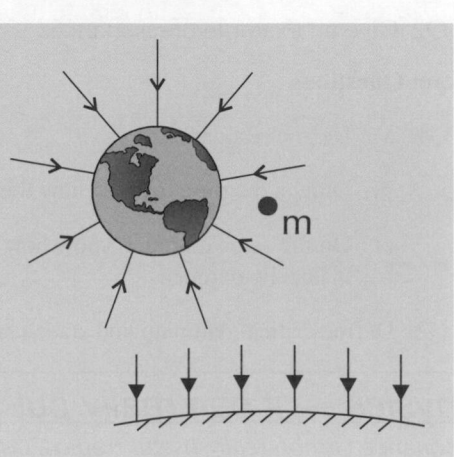

The officers weren't sure how to enforce the inverse square law.

You can Draw **Field Lines** to Show the **Field** Around an Object

Gravitational field lines (or **lines of force**) are arrows showing the **direction of the force** that masses would feel in a gravitational field.

1) If you put a small mass, ***m***, anywhere in the Earth's gravitational field, it will always be attracted **towards** the Earth.

2) The Earth's gravitational field is **radial** — the lines of force meet at the centre of the Earth.

3) If you move mass *m* further away from the Earth — where the **lines** of force are **further apart** — the **force** it experiences **decreases**.

4) The small mass, *m*, has a gravitational field of its own. This doesn't have a noticeable effect on the Earth though, because the Earth is so much **more massive**.

5) Close to the Earth's surface, the field is (almost) uniform — the **field lines** are (almost) **parallel** and **equally spaced**. You can usually **assume** that the field is perfectly uniform.

Gravitational Fields

The **Field Strength** is the **Force per Unit Mass**

Gravitational field strength, g, is the **force per unit mass**. Its value depends on **where you are** in the field.
There's a really simple equation for working it out:

$$g = \frac{F}{m}$$ g has units of newtons per kilogram (Nkg⁻¹)

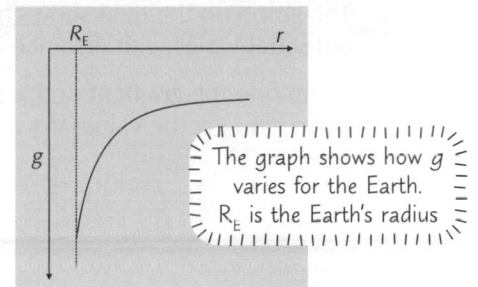

The **value** of **g** at the **Earth's surface** is approximately **9.81 Nkg⁻¹** (or 9.81 ms⁻²).

1) F is the force experienced by a mass m when it's placed in the gravitational field. Divide F by m and you get the **force per unit mass**.

2) g is a **vector** quantity, always pointing towards the centre of the mass whose field you're describing. Depending on the direction **defined** to be positive, it **could** be negative.

3) Since the gravitational field is **almost uniform** at the Earth's surface, you can assume g is a **constant** if you don't go too **high**.

4) g is just the **acceleration** of a mass in a gravitational field. It's often called the **acceleration due to gravity**.

In a **Radial Field**, **g** is **Inversely Proportional** to **r²**

Point masses have **radial** gravitational fields (see previous page).
The value of g depends on the distance r from the point mass M.

$$g = -\frac{GM}{r^2}$$ where g is the gravitational field strength (Nkg⁻¹)

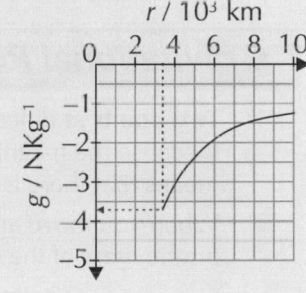

The graph shows how g varies for the Earth. R_E is the Earth's radius

And it's an **inverse square law** again — as **r increases**, **g decreases**.

Example: The graph shows how the gravitational field strength, g, varies with distance, r, from the centre of the planet Mars. The radius of Mars is approximately 3.4×10^3 km. Estimate the mass of Mars.

You can see from the graph that the value of g at the surface of Mars is about −3.7 Nkg⁻¹.

Rearrange the formula: $g = -\frac{GM}{r^2}$ to find M, then stick the values in
— don't forget to convert to standard units first.

So, $M = -\frac{gr^2}{G} = -\frac{-3.7 \times (3.4 \times 10^6)^2}{6.67 \times 10^{-11}} = 6.4 \times 10^{23}$ **kg (to 2 s.f.)**.

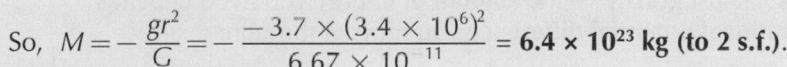

Practice Questions

Q1 Draw a diagram showing the Earth's gravitational field close to its surface. State the assumption made.
Q2 Define gravitational field strength and write an equation linking it to force.

Exam Questions

Acceleration due to gravity on Earth g = 9.81 ms⁻², R_E = 6400 km

Q1   Calculate the mass of Earth.   [2 marks]

Q2   The Moon has a mass of 7.35×10^{22} kg and a radius of 1740 km.

   a)   Calculate the value of g at the Moon's surface.   [1 mark]

   b)   Calculate the gravitational force on a 25 kg object 10 m (to 2 s.f.) above the surface of the Moon.   [2 marks]

Q3   A satellite is orbiting Earth and experiences a gravitational field strength of g = 4 Nkg⁻¹. The radius of its orbit is then increased until it experiences a gravitational field strength of g = 2 Nkg⁻¹. Choose the option which describes the factor by which the radius of orbit has been increased, correct to 2 s.f.

   A   1.2   B   1.4   C   1.6   D   1.8   [1 mark]

If you're really stuck, put 'Inverse Square Law'...

Clever chap, Newton, but famously tetchy. He got into fights with other physicists, mainly over planetary motion and calculus... the usual playground squabbles. Then he spent the rest of his life trying to turn scrap metal into gold. Weird.

Gravitational Potential and Energy

Gravitational potential is all to do with the energy something has based on where it is in a gravitational field.

Gravitational Potential is the Work Done to Move a Unit Mass from 'Infinity'

1) The **gravitational potential**, V_g, at a point is the work done in moving a **unit mass** from **infinity** to that **point**.

2) In a **radial field** (like the Earth's), the equation for gravitational potential is:

$$V_g = -\frac{GM}{r}$$

V_g is gravitational potential (Jkg⁻¹), G is the gravitational constant, M is the mass of the object causing the gravitational field (kg), and r is the distance from the centre of the object (m).

> **Gravitational potential** is **negative** — you have to **do work against** the **gravitational field** to move an object out of it. The **further** you are from the centre of a radial field, the **smaller** the magnitude of V_g. At an **infinite distance** from the mass, the gravitational potential will be **zero**.

3) The graph on the right shows how **gravitational potential** varies with **distance** from the Earth.

4) If you find the **gradient** of this graph at a particular point, you get the value of g at that point.

5) Since $g = -\frac{GM}{r^2}$ and $V_g - \frac{GM}{r}$, we can see that $g = \frac{V_g}{r}$.

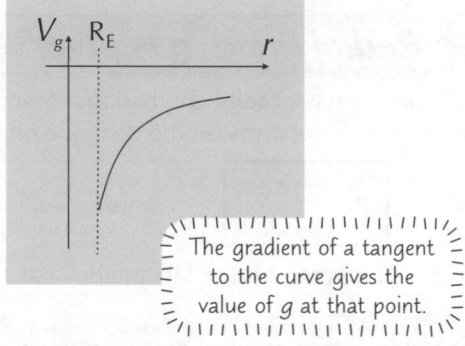

> The gradient of a tangent to the curve gives the value of g at that point.

Gravitational Potential Difference is the Work Done Moving a Unit Mass

1) **Two points** at different distances from a mass will have **different** gravitational potentials (because the magnitude of the gravitational potential decreases with distance) — this means that there is a **gravitational potential difference** between these two points.

2) When you **move** an object you do **work** against **gravity** — the **amount of energy** you need depends on the **mass** of the object and the **gravitational potential difference** you move it through:

$$\Delta W = m\Delta V_g$$

where ΔW is the work done (J), m is the mass of the object (kg) and ΔV_g is the gravitational potential difference (Jkg⁻¹).

3) The graph shows how the **force** on an object, due to the **gravitational field** of a **point mass**, varies with the object's **distance**, r, from the point mass.

4) The **area** under the curve between two values of r gives the **work done** to **move** the object from one point to the other.

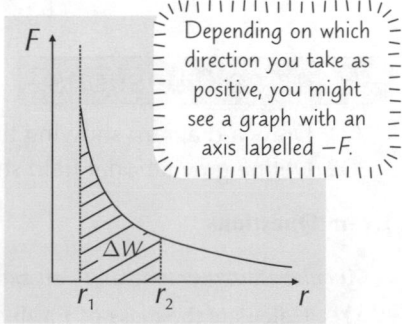

> Depending on which direction you take as positive, you might see a graph with an axis labelled $-F$.

An Object's Gravitational Potential Energy Depends on its Mass

1) **Gravitational potential** is work done per unit mass, so the **gravitational potential energy** (E) of an object at a point in a gravitational field is:

$$E = mV_g$$

2) Substituting in the formula for V_g, the gravitational potential energy of an object of mass m is:

$$E = m\left(-\frac{GM}{r}\right) = -\frac{GMm}{r}$$

E is gravitational potential energy (J), and r is the distance from the centre of M to the centre of m (m).

Gravitational Potential and Energy

To Escape a **Gravitational Field**, a Mass must Travel at the **Escape Velocity**

The **escape velocity** is defined as the velocity needed so an object has **just enough** kinetic energy to escape a gravitational field. This is when an object's **kinetic energy** is **equal** and **opposite** to its **gravitational potential energy** — so the **total energy** is **zero**. The formula for **escape velocity** is:

$$v = \sqrt{\frac{2GM}{r}}$$

v is escape velocity (ms⁻¹)

Deriving Escape Velocity

1) As you know total energy (kinetic energy + gravitational potential energy) is **zero**:

$$\frac{1}{2}mv^2 + \left(-\frac{GMm}{r}\right) = 0 \quad \text{so} \quad \frac{1}{2}mv^2 = \frac{GMm}{r}$$

2) **Cancel** the m's.

$$\frac{1}{2}v^2 = \frac{GM}{r}$$

The escape velocity is the same for all masses in the same gravitational field.

3) **Rearrange** for velocity, v:

$$v^2 = \frac{2GM}{r} \longrightarrow v - \sqrt{\frac{2GM}{r}}$$

No matter how fast he ran, Luke couldn't escape exams.

Example: Find the escape velocity on Earth. Mass of Earth = 5.98×10^{24} kg, radius of Earth = 6.37×10^6 m and $G = 6.67 \times 10^{-11}$ Nm²kg⁻².

Simply substitute in the given values.

$$v = \sqrt{\frac{2GM}{r}} = \sqrt{\frac{2 \times 6.67 \times 10^{-11} \times 5.98 \times 10^{24}}{6.37 \times 10^6}} = 11\,190.7\ldots = \mathbf{11\,200\ ms^{-1}}\ \textbf{(to 3 s.f.)}$$

This means you'd have to throw a ball upwards at 11.2 kms⁻¹ for it to fully escape Earth's pull. That's probably faster than you can manage.

Practice Questions

Q1 What is gravitational potential? Write an equation for it.

Q2 Sketch a graph of gravitational potential against distance for the Earth. What does the gradient of this graph describe?

Q3 Write down the equation for calculating the work done by moving a unit mass through a gravitational potential.

Q4 Describe how you get from the gravitational potential to gravitational potential energy.

Q5 What is the escape velocity? Write an equation for it.

Exam Question

Q1 A 300 kg probe is sent to an asteroid to collect rock samples before returning to Earth. The asteroid has a mass of 2.67×10^{19} kg.

a) The gravitational potential, V_g, at the surface of the asteroid is -1.52×10^4 Jkg⁻¹. Calculate the radius of the asteroid. [2 marks]

b) Calculate the speed at which an object would need to be launched from the surface of the asteroid for it to fully escape its gravitational field. [1 mark]

c) Calculate the work done by the probe as it travels from the surface to a point 2000 m above the surface. [3 marks]

With enough work you have the potential for brilliance...

So quite a lot of new stuff here, but hopefully you can see how everything links together. It's all to do with energy — you do work to change your gravitational potential energy, and you need to make your kinetic energy equal your gravitational potential energy in order to escape a gravitational field. Now time to start learning all of those equations.

Motion of Masses in Gravitational Fields

Planets just go round and round in circles. Well, ellipses really, but I won't tell if you don't...

Planets are Satellites which Orbit the Sun

1) A **satellite** is just any **smaller mass** which **orbits** a **much larger mass** — the **Moon** is a satellite of the Earth.

2) In our Solar System, the planets have **nearly circular orbits**... so you can use the **equations of circular motion**.

The Speed of an Orbit depends on its Radius and the Mass of the Larger Body

1) Earth feels a force due to the gravitational 'pull' of the **Sun**. This force is given by Newton's law of gravitation...

$$F = -\frac{GMm}{r^2}$$

(see p.22)

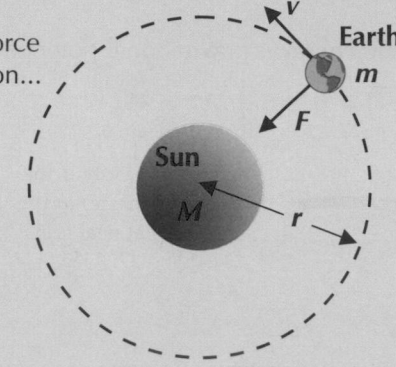

2) The Earth has velocity v. Its linear speed is constant but its **direction** is not — so it's accelerating. The **centripetal force** (p.14) causing this acceleration is:

$$F = \frac{mv^2}{r}$$

3) The **centripetal force** on the Earth must be a result of the **gravitational force** due to the Sun, and so these forces must be **equal**...

$$\frac{mv^2}{r} = \frac{GMm}{r^2} \quad \text{and rearranging...} \quad \boxed{v = \sqrt{\frac{GM}{r}}}$$

v is orbital speed (ms^{-1}),
G is the gravitational constant, 6.67×10^{-11} Nm^{2}kg^{-2},
M is the mass of the object being orbited (kg),
r is the distance from the centre of the object being orbited to the centre of the orbiting satellite (m).

And the Period does too

The **time** taken **for one orbit** is called the **period, T**. For circular motion $T = \frac{2\pi r}{v}$.

Substitute $v = \sqrt{\frac{GM}{r}}$ and rearrange... $\boxed{T^2 = \left(\frac{4\pi^2}{GM}\right)r^3}$ T is the period (s).

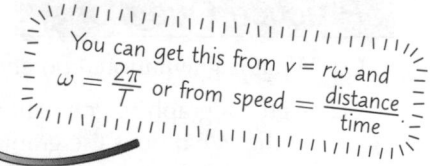

You can get this from $v = r\omega$ and $\omega = \frac{2\pi}{T}$ or from $speed = \frac{distance}{time}$.

Example: The Moon takes 27.3 days (2.36×10^6 s) to orbit the Earth. Calculate its distance from the Earth. Take the mass of the Earth to be 5.975×10^{24} kg.

You're trying to find the radius of the orbit, r. Use the formula for the period, T, and rearrange it for r^3:

$$r^3 = \frac{T^2 GM}{4\pi^2} = \frac{(2.36 \times 10^6)^2 \times 6.67 \times 10^{-11} \times 5.975 \times 10^{24}}{4\pi^2} = 5.62... \times 10^{25}$$

Then take the cube root: $r = \sqrt[3]{5.62... \times 10^{25}} = 3.830... \times 10^8 = \mathbf{3.83 \times 10^8}$ **m (to 3 s.f.)**

(this is the distance between the centre of the Earth and the centre of the Moon)

Geostationary Satellites Orbit the Earth once in 24 Hours

1) Geostationary satellites orbit directly over the **equator** and are **always above the same point** on Earth.

2) A geostationary satellite travels at the **same angular speed as the Earth** turns below it.

3) Their orbit takes exactly **one day**.

4) These satellites are really useful for sending TV and telephone signals and have improved **communication** around the world. The satellite is **stationary** relative to a certain point on the Earth, so you don't have to alter the angle of your receiver (or transmitter) to keep up.

5) There are downsides though — they are **expensive** and pose a **small** risk of something going **wrong** and the satellite **falling** back to Earth.

Motion of Masses in Gravitational Fields

Kepler's Laws are about the Motion of Planets in the Solar System

Kepler came up with these three laws around 1600, about 80 years before Newton developed his law of gravitation. They're usually used to describe the planets in our solar system, but can be used for **any** object and its satellite.

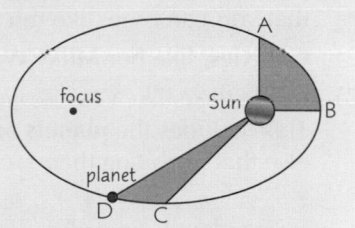

FIRST LAW: Each planet moves in an **ellipse** around the Sun, with the Sun at one **focus** (a circle is just a special kind of ellipse).

SECOND LAW: A line joining the Sun to a planet will sweep out **equal areas in equal times**. (So if moving from A to B takes the same amount of time as moving from C to D, the two shaded sections will have equal areas.)

THIRD LAW: The **period** of the orbit and the **mean distance** between the Sun and the planet are related by **Kepler's third law**: $\boxed{T^2 \propto r^3}$

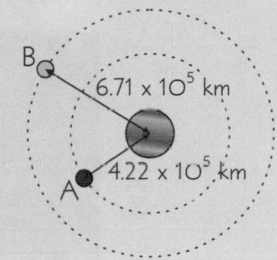

Example: The diagram shows the orbits of two exoplanets around a star in a nearby solar system. Exoplanet A completes one orbit of the star in 42.5 hours. Find the orbital period of exoplanet B to the nearest hour, assuming both orbits are circular.

Using Kepler's third law: $\dfrac{T_A^2}{r_A^3} = \dfrac{T_B^2}{r_B^3}$ so $T_B = \sqrt{\dfrac{T_A^2 r_B^3}{r_A^3}} = \sqrt{\dfrac{(42.5)^2 \times (6.71 \times 10^5)^3}{(4.22 \times 10^5)^3}}$

= 85 hours to the nearest hour

Atmospheric Thickness is also Linked to Gravity

1) As well as predicting the motion of satellites, **Newton's law of gravitation** can also help to explain how **thick** a planet's **atmosphere** is.

2) The planet's gravitational field exerts a **force** on everything around it, including the particles which make up its atmosphere. Otherwise, the particles would float off into **space**.

3) The more **massive** the planet is, the **larger** the force is further away from the planet's surface — so the more atmosphere particles it can stop escaping into space, leading to a **thicker atmosphere**.

Practice Questions

Q1 The International Space Station orbits the Earth with velocity v. If another vehicle docks with it, increasing its mass, what difference, if any, does this make to the speed or radius of the orbit?

Q2 Derive an expression for the radius of the orbit of a planet around the Sun, in terms of the period of its orbit.

Q3 State Kepler's three laws of planetary motion.

Q4 Explain why a massive planet would generally have a thicker atmosphere than a less massive planet of the same radius.

Exam Questions

$G = 6.67 \times 10^{-11} Nm^2kg^{-2}$, mass of Earth = 5.98×10^{24} kg, radius of Earth = 6400 km

Q1 a) A satellite orbits 200.0 km above the Earth's surface. Calculate the period of the satellite's orbit. [2 marks]

    b) What is the linear speed of the satellite? [1 mark]

Q2 At what height above the Earth's surface would a geostationary satellite orbit? [3 marks]

Q3 The Sun has a mass of 2.0×10^{30} kg, but loses mass at a rate of around 6×10^9 kgs^{-1}. Discuss whether this will have had any significant effect on the Earth's orbit over the past 50 000 years, supporting your answer with calculations. [2 marks]

All this talk of orbits is putting my head in a spin...

Kepler is sometimes proclaimed as the first science fiction writer. He wrote a tale about a fantastic trip to the Moon, where the book narrator's mum asks a demon the secret of space travel, to boldly go where — oh wait, different story. Unfortunately Kepler's book might have sparked an actual witch-hunt on Kepler's mum, whoops-a-daisy...

The Solar System & Astronomical Distances

Space is big. I mean, really big...

Our **Solar System** Contains More than just the **Sun** and **Planets**

1) The **universe** is **everything** that exists — this includes plenty you can see, like **stars** and **galaxies**, and plenty that you can't see, like **microwave radiation** (page 37), **dark energy** and **dark matter** (pages 38-39).

2) **Galaxies**, like our **Milky Way galaxy**, are clusters of **stars** and **planets** that are held together by gravity.

3) Inside the Milky Way is our **Solar System**, which consists of the **Sun** and all of the objects that **orbit** it. This includes the **planets** and their **planetary satellites** (including moons, artificial satellites and anything else that's orbiting them), **comets**, and **asteroids**.

> The planets (in order) are: **Mercury**, **Venus**, **Earth**, **Mars**, **Jupiter**, **Saturn**, **Uranus** and **Neptune**. The planets (and the asteroid belt) all have nearly **circular** orbits. Pluto is a dwarf planet beyond Neptune.

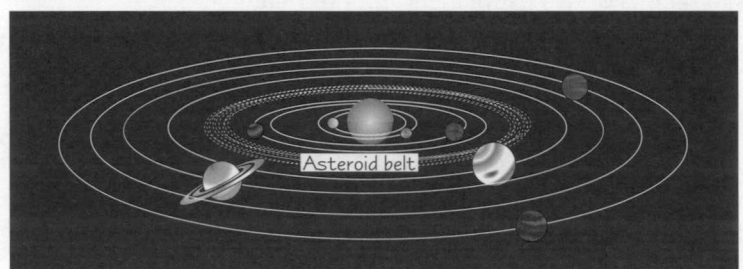

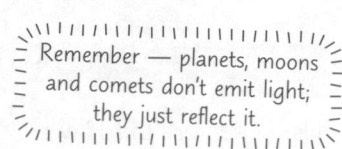
Remember — planets, moons and comets don't emit light; they just reflect it.

4) The orbits of the **comets** we see are **highly elliptical**. Comets are "**dirty snowballs**" that we think usually orbit the Sun about **1000 times further away** than **Pluto** does (in the "Oort cloud"). Occasionally one gets **dislodged** and heads towards the Sun. It follows a new elliptical orbit, which can take **millions of years** to complete. Some comets (from closer in than the Oort cloud) follow a **smaller orbit** and they return to swing round the Sun more regularly. The most famous is **Halley's comet**, which orbits in **76 years**.

Distances in the Solar System can be Measured in **Astronomical Units (AU)**

1) From **Copernicus** onwards, astronomers were able to work out the **distance** the **planets** are from the Sun **relative** to the Earth, using **astronomical units** (AU). But they could not work out the **actual distances**.

> One **astronomical unit (AU)** is defined as the **mean distance** between the **Earth** and the **Sun**.

2) The **size** of the AU wasn't known accurately until 1769 — when it was carefully **measured** during a **transit of Venus** (when Venus passed between the Earth and the Sun).

3) We now know that 1 AU is equal to about **150 million km**.

Another Measure of Astronomical Distance is the **Light-Year (ly)**

1) All **electromagnetic waves** travel at the **speed of light**, c, in a vacuum ($c = 3.00 \times 10^8$ ms^{-1}). The **distance** that electromagnetic waves travel through a vacuum in **one year** is called a **light-year** (ly). **1 ly** is equivalent to about **9.5×10^{15} m**.

2) If you see the light from a star that is, say, **10 light-years away** then you're actually seeing it as it was **10 years ago**. The further away the object is, the further **back in time** you are actually seeing it. So when we look at the stars we're looking **back in time**, and we can only see as far back as the **beginning of the universe**. This means we can work out the **size** of the **observable universe** (p.38).

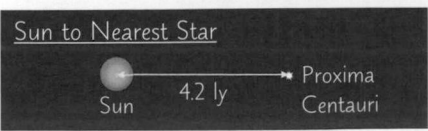

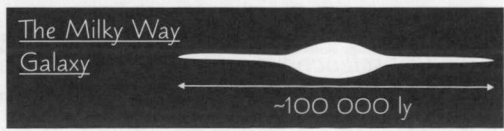

Though technically correct, Ida felt Karl's promise they'd be looking back in time had been slightly misleading.

The Solar System & Astronomical Distances

The Distance to Nearby Stars can be Measured in Parsecs

1) Imagine you're in a **moving car**. You see that (stationary) objects in the **foreground** seem to be **moving faster** than objects in the **distance**. This **apparent motion** is called **parallax**. Parallax is measured in terms of the **angle of parallax**. The **greater** the **angle**, the **nearer** the object is to you.

2) The same thing happens as the Earth orbits the Sun. At different points in the Earth's orbit, nearby stars appear to **move** relative to very distant stars.

3) By **measuring** the angle that a nearby star seems to move through as the Earth moves round its orbit, you can work out how far away the star is:

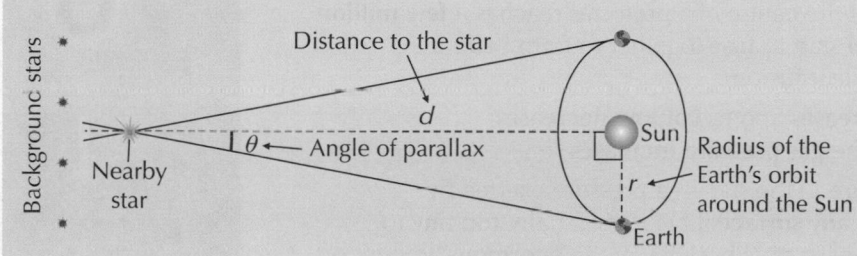

Using trig: $d = \frac{r}{\tan \theta}$.

For stars, θ is really small, so you can use the small angle approximation: $\tan \theta \approx \theta$ (where θ is in radians).

So $d \approx \frac{r}{\theta}$.

4) Calculating d in metres, or in AU, would give you some really big numbers. Instead, astronomers have defined a unit of distance from the angle of parallax. This unit is called a **parsec**.

> A star is exactly **one parsec (pc)** away from Earth if the **angle of parallax**, θ, as the Earth moves through 1 AU, is **1 second of arc** — that's $(1/3600)^{\circ}$.

5) This means the distance to a nearby star, in parsecs, is given by:

$$d = \frac{1}{p} \quad \text{so} \quad p = \frac{1}{d} \quad \text{where } p \text{ is the parallax, in arcseconds}$$

The clue's in the name: an object is 1 parsec away if the parallax is 1 arcsecond.

6) One parsec is about 3.1×10^{16} m. The nearest star to Earth (other than the Sun) is about 1.3 parsecs away.

Practice Questions

Q1 Describe what is meant by: a) the universe, b) the Milky Way.

Q2 Apart from the planets, what other components make up our Solar System?

Q3 Define an astronomical unit.

Q4 Describe what parallax is and explain how it allows us to measure the distances to nearby stars.

Exam Questions

Q1 Describe the main differences between the orbits of planets and comets in our Solar System. [2 marks]

Q2 a) State the definition of a light-year. [1 mark]

   b) Explain why looking at distant stars is like looking back in time. [2 marks]

Q3 A star has an angle of parallax of $(5 \times 10^{-5})^{\circ}$ when the Earth moves through 1 AU.

   a) Calculate the distance from the star to the Sun in parsecs. [2 marks]

   b) Calculate the distance from the star to the Sun in light years. [2 marks]

So — using a ruler's out of the question then...

Welcome to astrophysics, the best bit of Physics. Shame it starts with the maths, really. Make sure you know why we need the different measures used in astronomy (and you get how parsecs work — they're a bit tricky). You're given conversion factors for light-years and parsecs in the exam, but not AU, so repeat after me: 1 AU = 150 million kilometres.

Stellar Evolution

Stars go through several different stages in their lives — from clouds of dust and gas, to red giants to white dwarfs...

Stars Begin as Clouds of Dust and Gas

1) Stars are born in a **cloud** of interstellar **dust** and **gas**, most of which was left when previous stars blew themselves apart in **supernovae**. The denser clumps of the cloud **contract** (very slowly) under the force of **gravity**.

2) When these clumps get dense enough, the cloud fragments into regions called **protostars**, that continue to contract and **heat up**.

3) Eventually the **temperature** at the centre of a protostar reaches a **few million degrees**, and **hydrogen nuclei** start to **fuse** together to form helium (see page 79 for more on nuclear fusion).

4) As the star's **temperature increases** and its **volume decreases** (remember, its contracting), the **gas pressure increases** (p.9)

5) There is also **radiation pressure** in the star — a pressure exerted by electromagnetic radiation on **any surface** it hits. It's usually **too tiny** to notice, but becomes significant in stars because of the **enormous** amount of **electromagnetic radiation** released by **fusion**.

6) The combination of gas pressure and radiation pressure counteract the force of gravity, preventing the star from contracting further.

7) The star has now reached the **MAIN SEQUENCE** and will stay there, relatively **unchanged**, while it fuses hydrogen into helium.

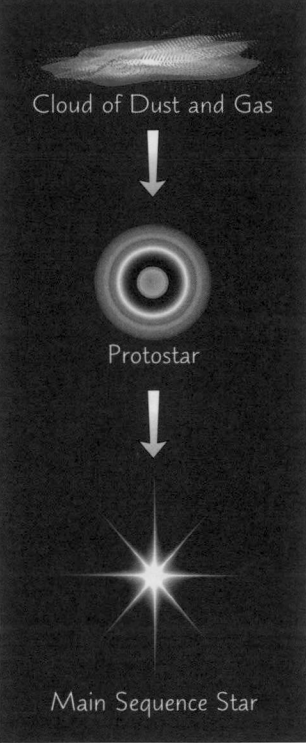

Cloud of Dust and Gas

Protostar

Main Sequence Star

Main Sequence Stars become Red Giants when they Run Out of Fuel

1) Stars spend most of their lives as **main sequence** stars. The **pressure** produced from **hydrogen fusion** in their **core balances** the **gravitational force** trying to compress them. This stage is called **core hydrogen burning**.

2) When the **hydrogen** in the **core** runs out, nuclear fusion **stops**, and with it the **outward pressure stops**. The core **contracts** and **heats up** under the **weight** of the star. The outer layers expand and cool, and the star becomes a **RED GIANT**.

3) The material **surrounding** the core still has **plenty of hydrogen**. The **heat** from the contracting **core** raises the **temperature** of this material enough for the hydrogen to **fuse**. This is called **shell hydrogen burning**. (Very low-mass stars stop at this point. They use up their fuel and slowly fade away...)

4) The core continues to contract until, eventually, it gets **hot** enough and **dense** enough for **helium** to **fuse** into **carbon** and **oxygen**. This is called **core helium burning**. This releases a **huge** amount of energy, which **pushes** the **outer layers** of the star outwards.

5) When the **helium** runs out, the carbon-oxygen core **contracts again** and heats a **shell** around it so that helium can fuse in this region — **shell helium burning**.

Low Mass Stars (like the Sun) Eject their Shells, leaving behind a White Dwarf

1) In low-mass stars, the **carbon-oxygen core isn't hot enough** for any further **fusion** and so it continues to **contract** under its own **weight**. Once the core has shrunk to about **Earth-size**, **electrons** exert enough pressure (**electron degeneracy pressure**) to stop it collapsing any more (fret not — you don't have to know how).

2) This only works for stars with a core mass under about 1.4 times the mass of the sun though — in bigger stars the electron degeneracy pressure **isn't enough** to counteract the gravitational force and the star collapses (see next page). The maximum mass for which the electron degeneracy pressure can counteract the gravitational force is called the **Chandrasekhar limit**.

3) For stars below the Chandrasekhar limit, the **helium shell** becomes increasingly **unstable** as the core contracts. The star **pulsates** and **ejects** its outer layers into space as a **planetary nebula**, leaving behind the dense core.

4) The star is now a very **hot**, **dense solid** called a **WHITE DWARF**, which will simply **cool down** and **fade away**.

Stellar Evolution

The *Sun* is a *Main Sequence Star*

The **Sun** might seem quite **special** to us on Earth — it's the reason we're all here after all. But it's just like any other **low mass star** — it started off as a **cloud of dust and gas** and evolved to be the **main sequence star** we see today. Of course, this means it will most likely become a **red giant** and then finally fizzle out as a **white dwarf** — sob.

Massive Stars have a *Shorter Life* and a more *Exciting Death*

The **mass** of a star will determine how it **evolves**. **Low to medium mass** stars (like the **Sun**) follow the sequence above. **High mass stars** follow the **sequence below**.

1) Stars with a **large mass** have a **lot of fuel**, but they use it up **more quickly** and don't spend so long as main sequence stars.

2) When they are **red giants** the **'core burning to shell burning'** process can continue beyond the fusion of helium, building up layers in an **onion-like structure** to become **SUPER RED GIANTS** (or red super giants).

3) For **really massive** stars, fusion can go all the way up to **iron**. Nuclear fusion **beyond iron** isn't **energetically favourable** (p.76), so once an iron core is formed then very quickly it's goodbye star...

4) When the core of a star runs out of fuel, it starts to **contract**, forming a **white dwarf** core.

5) If the star's core is larger than the **Chandrasekhar limit**, **electron degeneracy pressure** can't stop the core contracting. This happens when the mass of the core is more than **1.4 times** the mass of the Sun. The core of the star continues to **contract**, and as it does, the **outer layers fall in** and **rebound** off the core, setting up huge **shock waves**. These shock waves cause the star to **explode** cataclysmically in a **SUPERNOVA**, leaving behind a **NEUTRON STAR** or (if the star was massive enough) a **BLACK HOLE**. The light from a supernova can briefly outshine an entire galaxy.

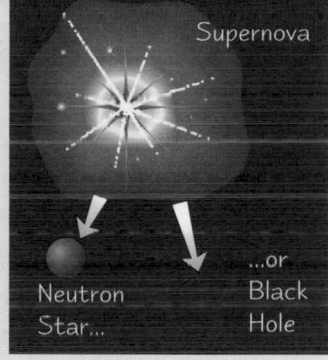

Neutron Stars are *Very Dense...*

1) As the core of a massive star contracts, electrons get squashed onto the atomic **nuclei**, combining with protons to form **neutrons** and **neutrinos** (hence the name 'neutron star'). If a white dwarf's core is 1.4 to 3 times the mass of the Sun then this is as far as the star can contract. The core suddenly collapses to a **neutron star**, causing a **supernova**.

2) **Neutron stars** are incredibly **dense** (about 4×10^{17} kgm^{-3}). They're also **very small**, typically about 20 km across, and they can **rotate very fast** (up to 600 times a second).

3) They emit **radio waves** in two beams as they rotate. These beams sometimes sweep past the Earth and can be observed as **radio pulses** rather like the flashes of a lighthouse. These rotating neutron stars are called **PULSARS**.

... But Not as Dense as *Black Holes*

1) If the **core** of a star is more than **3 times** the Sun's mass, the neutrons can't withstand the gravitational forces and the star continues to **collapse**.

2) For something of this size, there are **no known mechanisms** left to stop the core collapsing to an **infinitely dense** point called a **singularity**. At that point, the **laws of physics** break down completely.

3) Up to a certain distance away the gravitational pull is **so strong** that nothing, not even **light**, can escape its grasp — it's called a **black hole**. The **boundary** of this region is called the **event horizon**.

Elle wasn't sure she wanted to be the star player anymore if this was how it would end...

Stellar Evolution

Luminosity vs Temperature — the H-R Diagram

1) **Luminosity** is a measure of how **bright** an object is (p.34). If you plot **luminosity** against **temperature** for stars, you don't just get a random collection of dots. The stars appear to group in **distinct areas** on the plot.

2) The distinct areas show the main stages of a star's life cycle: the **main sequence**, **red giants**, **super red giants** and **white dwarfs** (see previous pages). This is called the **Hertzsprung-Russell diagram**. ⟹

3) The reason you can see these areas is because stars exist in these **stable** stages of their life cycle for **long periods of time**. You don't see groups of stars in any transitional period on the H-R diagram because they are unstable and the transitions happen **quickly** (compared with the life of the star).

Temperature goes the "wrong way" along the horizontal axis — from hotter to cooler.

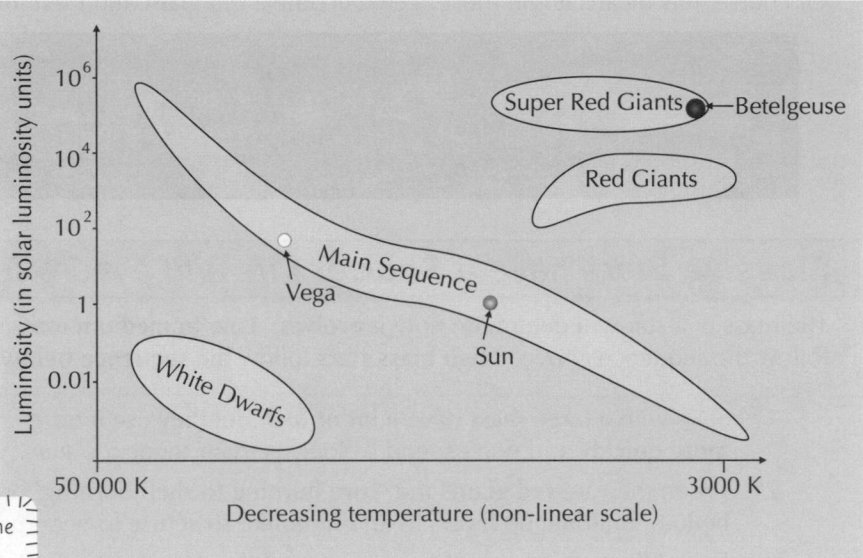

Practice Questions

Q1 How are stars formed? Describe the two forms of pressure that prevent a star at the beginning of its main sequence from collapsing due to gravity and explain what causes them.

Q2 What causes a star to evolve from the main sequence to become a red giant?

Q3 What causes a supernova?

Q4 Describe a white dwarf and a neutron star. What are the main differences between them?

Q5 Describe briefly what is meant by a black hole.

Q6 What is a H-R diagram a plot of? What four main types of star are shown on a H-R diagram?

Exam Questions

Q1 a) Describe what is meant by the Chandrasekhar limit. [1 mark]

b)* Describe and explain the main similarities and differences between the evolution of high mass and low mass stars, starting from the beginning of their main sequence. [6 marks]

Q2 Antares is a super red giant in the constellation Scorpius.

State the letter (A, B, C, D or E) on the Hertzsprung-Russell diagram on the right that represents Antares.

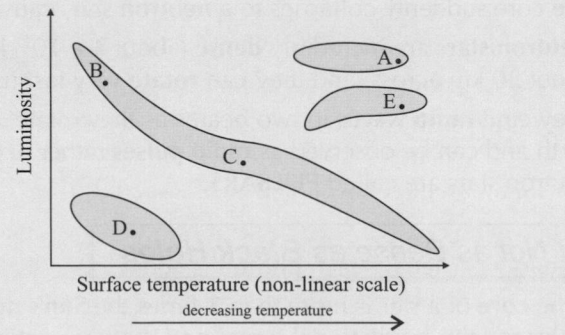

[1 mark]

*The quality of your extended response will be assessed in this question.

Live fast, die young, burn bright...

The more massive a star, the more spectacular its life cycle. The most massive stars burn up the hydrogen in their core so quickly that they only live for a fraction of the Sun's lifetime — but when they go, they do it in style. Make sure you know all the stages in the life cycles of stars of different sizes, and where they all fit in on the H-R diagram.

Spectra from Stars

'Twinkle, twinkle little star, how I wonder what you are'... well if you really want to know, you can look at the star's spectrum. It'll help if you know the regions of the EM spectrum before you start.

You Can Use a **Diffraction Grating** to find the **Wavelength** of Light

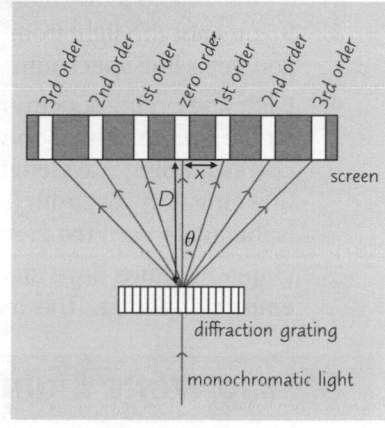

1) If you shine **monochromatic light** (light with a single wavelength or frequency) through a diffraction grating, you'll get a pattern of **bright lines** (maxima) on a dark background. This is a result of the light **interfering** with itself constructively and destructively (you met interference in year 1 of A-level).

2) The line of **maximum brightness** at the centre is called the **zero order** line, the next lines on **each side** are called **first order lines**, and so on.

3) Using the **fringe width** (the distance **between** the maxima), **x**, and the distance to the screen, **D**, the angle the first order line makes with the zero order line can be calculated using the **small angle approximation**: $\Rightarrow$

$$\theta \approx \tan \theta = \frac{x}{D}$$

4) If you know the slit separation, **d**, the order of the maximum you're observing, **n**, and the angle between this maximum and the incident light, **θ**, you can find the **wavelength** of the incident light:

$$d \sin \theta = n\lambda$$

If $\sin \theta > 1$, then that maximum doesn't exist.

You might see these called 'transmission diffraction gratings'. This just means they let light through.

Continuous Spectra Contain All Possible Wavelengths

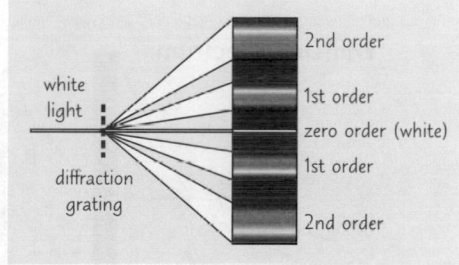

1) The **spectrum** of **white light** is **continuous**.

2) If you **split** white **light** up with a **diffraction grating**, the **different wavelengths** within the white light are **diffracted** by **different** amounts.

3) Each **order** in the pattern becomes a **spectrum**, with **red** on the **outside** and **violet** on the **inside**. The **zero order maximum** stays **white** because all the wavelengths just pass straight through.

4) **Hot things** emit a **continuous spectrum** in the visible and infrared regions. If an object is hot enough, the spectrum can reach into shorter wavelengths, like **ultraviolet**.

Electrons in Atoms Exist in Discrete Energy Levels

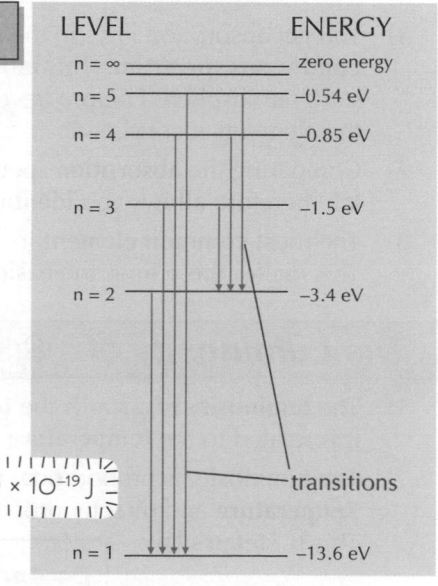

1) **Electrons** in an **atom** can **only exist** in certain **well-defined energy levels**. Each level is given a **number**, with **n = 1** representing the **ground state**.

2) Electrons can **move down** an energy level by **emitting** a **photon**.

3) Since these **transitions** are between **definite energy levels**, the **energy** of **each photon** emitted can **only** take a **certain allowed value**.

4) The diagram on the right shows the **energy levels** for **atomic hydrogen** (the energies are all negative because of how 'zero energy' is defined.)

5) The **energy** carried by each **photon** is **equal** to the **difference in energies** between the **two levels**. It's given by the equation:

$$\Delta E = hf = \frac{hc}{\lambda}$$

where *h* is the Planck constant, 6.63×10^{-34} Js^{-1}, *c* is the speed of light, 3.00×10^8 ms^{-1}, λ is the photon's wavelength and *f* is the photon's frequency

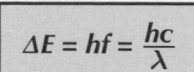

1 eV = 1.60×10^{-19} J

Spectra from Stars

Hot Gases Produce Line Emission Spectra

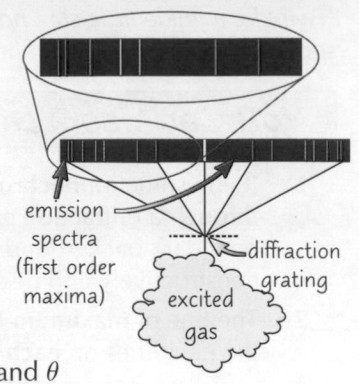

1) If you heat a gas to a high temperature, many of its electrons move to **higher energy levels**.

2) As they fall back to the ground state, these electrons emit energy as **photons**.

3) If you **split** the light from a **hot gas** with a **diffraction grating**, you get a **line spectrum**.

4) Each **line** on the spectrum corresponds to a **particular wavelength** of light **emitted** by the source. Since only **certain photon energies** are **allowed**, you only see the **corresponding wavelengths**. You can calculate the wavelength, λ, of each line in a line emission spectrum using $d \sin \theta = n\lambda$ (where d is the slit spacing of the grating and θ is the angle from the zero order line), if you know which order maxima the spectrum is.

5) Different **atoms** have different electron **energy levels** and so different sets of **emission spectra**. This means you can **identify** a gas from its **emission spectrum**.

Shining White Light through a Cool Gas gives an Absorption Spectrum

1) You get a **line absorption spectrum** when **light** with a **continuous spectrum** of **energy** (white light) passes through a cool gas:

   - At **low temperatures**, **most** of the **electrons** in the **gas atoms** will be in their **ground states**.
   - **Photons** of the **correct wavelength** are **absorbed** by the **electrons** to **excite** them to **higher energy levels**.
   - These **wavelengths** are **missing** from the **continuous spectrum** when it **comes out** on the other side.
   - You see a **continuous spectrum** with **black lines** in it corresponding to the **absorbed wavelengths**.

2) If you **compare** the **absorption** and **emission spectra** of a **particular gas**, the **black lines** in the **absorption spectrum match up** to the **bright lines** in the **emission spectrum**.

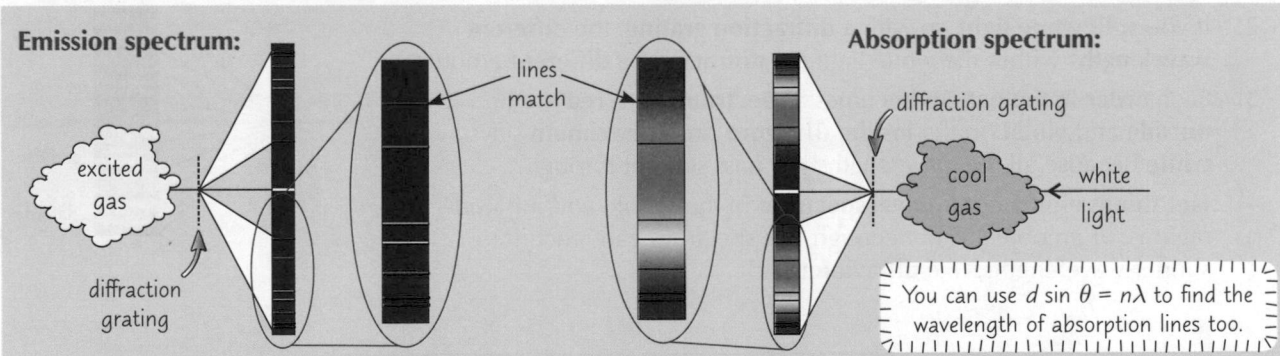

You can use $d \sin \theta = n\lambda$ to find the wavelength of absorption lines too.

3) You get absorption lines in the spectra of light from **stars**. Stars can be assumed to emit radiation in a **continuous spectrum**. This radiation has to pass through a **large amount** of gas at the surface of the star (the star's 'atmosphere') before travelling to Earth. This gas **absorbs** particular wavelengths of light depending on the elements it consists of.

4) Comparing the **absorption** spectra of **stars** to sets of **emission** spectral lines from the **lab** therefore allows you **identify elements** within a star.

5) The most **common element** in most stars is **hydrogen**, so the spectral lines for hydrogen are usually the **clearest**. This makes these lines the **easiest** to identify and measure.

The Luminosity of a Star Depends on its Temperature and Surface Area

1) The **luminosity** of a star is the **total energy** it emits **per second** i.e. its **power output**. It is related to the **temperature** of the star and its **surface area**.

2) The luminosity is proportional to the **fourth power** of the star's **temperature** and directly proportional to its surface area. This is **Stefan's law**:

$$L = 4\pi r^2 \sigma T^4$$

Where L is the luminosity of the star (in W), r is its radius (in m), T is its surface temperature (in K) and σ (a lower case 'sigma') is the Stefan constant.

3) Measurements give the Stefan constant as $\sigma = 5.67 \times 10^{-8} \ \text{Wm}^{-2}\text{K}^{-4}$.

MODULE 5: SECTION 4 — ASTROPHYSICS & COSMOLOGY

Spectra from Stars

The **Peak Wavelength** of a Star Depends on its **Temperature**

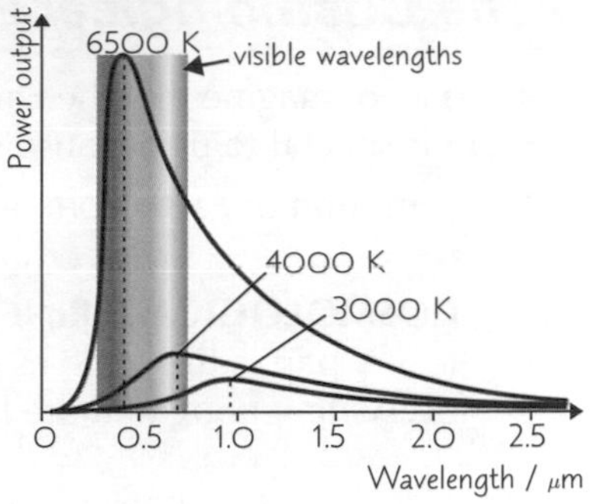

1) Objects emit **electromagnetic radiation** due to their **temperature**. At everyday temperatures this is mostly in the **infrared** part of the spectrum (which we can't see). But heat something up enough and it will start to **glow**.

2) **Stars** can be assumed to emit radiation in a **continuous spectrum**.

3) The relationship between **intensity** ('power per unit area') and **wavelength** for this radiation varies with **temperature**, as shown in the graph:

4) The most common wavelength becomes shorter as the surface temperature of the star increases. This is called the **peak wavelength**, λ_{max}.

5) You can use λ_{max} to estimate a star's **peak surface temperature** using **Wien's displacement law**:

$$\lambda_{max} \propto \frac{1}{T}$$

Where T is the temperature in kelvins.

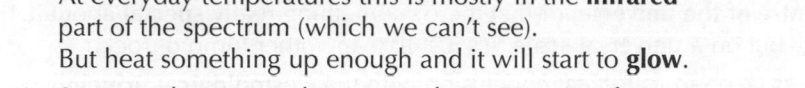

You can combine Stefan's law (see previous page) and Wien's displacement law to estimate a star's **radius**:

Example: Sirius A is a main sequence star, and Sirius B is a white dwarf. Sirius A has a surface temperature of 9800 K and produces electromagnetic radiation with a peak wavelength of 300 nm (to 2 s.f.). Sirius B has a luminosity of 9.4×10^{24} W and produces electromagnetic radiation with a peak wavelength of 115 nm. Estimate the radius of Sirius B.

First, find the temperature of Sirius B. $\lambda_{max} \propto \frac{1}{T}$, so $T\lambda_{max}$ = constant.

This means $T_A \lambda_{max\,A} = T_B \lambda_{max\,B}$ so $9800 \times 300 \times 10^{-9} = (115 \times 10^{-9})T_B$. So $T_B = \dfrac{9800 \times (300 \times 10^{-9})}{115 \times 10^{-9}} = 25\,565.2... $ K

Then use Stefan's law to find the star's radius:

$$L = 4\pi r^2 \sigma T^4 \text{ so } r = \sqrt{\frac{L}{4\pi\sigma T^4}} = \sqrt{\frac{9.4 \times 10^{24}}{4\pi \times (5.67 \times 10^{-8}) \times 25\,565.21...^4}} = \mathbf{5.6 \times 10^6 \text{ m (to 2 s.f.)}}$$

Practice Questions

Q1 Using the diagram on page 33 find the change in energy for an electron moving from n = 2 to n = 3 in an atom of atomic hydrogen. Indicate whether the change is positive or negative.

Q2 Describe how line emission and line absorption spectra are formed.

Q3 How can the line absorption spectrum of a star be used to identify elements within it?

Q4 Describe how the radiation emitted by a star varies with its temperature.

Exam Question

Q1 A scientist is investigating light from the Sun. She uses a telescope to pass light from the Sun through a diffraction grating with a slit separation of 8.3×10^{-7} m, and observes a first order absorption line at 30.0° from the zero order line.

a) Calculate the wavelength of light that this absorption line corresponds to. [1 mark]

b) Explain why photons of certain wavelengths are absorbed by atoms in the Sun's atmosphere. [2 marks]

c) Calculate the energy of the photon that has been absorbed to produce the line observed at 30.0°. [1 mark]

d) The scientist records the peak wavelength in sunlight as 490 nm. Given that the star Rigel has a surface temperature of 12 000 K, and a peak wavelength of 240 nm, estimate the peak temperature of the surface of the Sun. [2 marks]

e) The diameter of the Sun is about 1.4×10^9 m. Estimate the Sun's luminosity. [1 mark]

Who knew light could tell you so much...

This is some pretty tricky stuff, but it's also pretty cool. Just by looking at a star, you can tell what it's made of, how hot it is, and how big it is. Not too shabby. This is one of the hardest bits in this section, so take your time, and make sure you really understand it before you move on.

The Big Bang Theory

Everyone's heard of the Big Bang theory — well here's some evidence for it.

The **Cosmological Principle** Says the Whole **Universe** Obeys the **Same Laws**

It's easy to imagine that the Earth is at the **centre of the universe**, or that there's something really **special** about it. **Earth** is special to us because we **live here** — but on a **universal scale**, it's just like any other lump of rock.

The **demotion** of **Earth** from anything special is taken to its logical conclusion with the **Cosmological principle**:

> **COSMOLOGICAL PRINCIPLE:** on a **large scale** the universe is **homogeneous** (every part is the same as every other part) and **isotropic** (it looks the same in every direction), and the laws of physics are **universal** (the same everywhere).

This is a powerful idea — it means we can apply what we know about physics on the Earth and in our Solar System to the **rest of the universe**.

The **Doppler Effect** — the **Motion** of a Wave's **Source** Affects its **Wavelength**

1) Imagine an ambulance driving past you. As it moves **towards you**, its siren sounds **higher-pitched**, but as it **moves away**, its **pitch** is **lower**. This change in **frequency** and **wavelength** is called the **Doppler shift**.

2) The frequency and the wavelength **change** because the waves **bunch together** in **front** of the source and **stretch out behind** it. The **amount** of stretching or bunching together depends on the **velocity** of the **source**.

3) This happens with light too — when a **light source** moves **away** from us, the wavelengths become **longer** and the frequencies become lower. This shifts the light towards the **red** end of the spectrum and is called **red shift**.

4) When a light source moves **towards** us, the **opposite** happens and the light undergoes **blue shift**.

Putting that sock in with the white wash had caused a definite red shift in the girls' football kits.

5) The amount of red shift or blue shift is determined by the following formula:

$$\frac{\Delta\lambda}{\lambda} \approx \frac{\Delta f}{f} \approx \frac{v}{c}$$

$\Delta\lambda$ is the difference between the observed and emitted wavelengths, λ is the emitted wavelength, Δf is the difference between the observed and emitted frequencies, f is the emitted frequency, v is the velocity of the source in the observer's direction and c is the speed of light.

Red Shift Shows That the **Universe** is **Expanding**

1) Until the early 20th century, cosmologists believed that the Universe was **infinite** in both **space** and **time** (that is, it had always existed) and **static**. This seemed the **only way** it could be **stable**.

2) This changed when Edwin Hubble realised that the **spectra** from **galaxies** (apart from a few very close ones) all show **red shift** — so they're all **moving away** from us. The amount of **galactic red shift** gives the **recessional velocity** — how fast the galaxy is moving away.

Some nearby galaxies are moving towards us due to gravitational attraction. The light from these galaxies shows blue shift.

3) Plotting **recessional velocity** against **distance** shows that they're **proportional** — i.e. the **speed** that **galaxies move away** from us depends on **how far** away they are.

4) This suggests that the universe is **expanding**, and gives rise to **Hubble's law**:

$$v = H_0 d$$

Where v = recessional velocity in kms^{-1}, d = distance in Mpc and H_0 = Hubble's constant in kms^{-1}Mpc^{-1}.

5) Since distance is very difficult to measure, astronomers used to **disagree** greatly on the value of H_0, with measurements ranging from 50 to 100 km s^{-1} Mpc^{-1}. It's now generally accepted that H_0 lies **between 65 and 80 km s^{-1} Mpc^{-1}** and most agree it's around the **mid to low 70s**. You'll be given a value to use in the exam.

6) The **SI unit** for H_0 is s^{-1}. To get H_0 in SI units, you need v in ms^{-1} and d in m (1 Mpc = 3.1 × 10^{22} m).

The Big Bang Theory

The **Expanding Universe** gives rise to the **Big Bang Model**

The universe is **expanding** (as you know from the previous page) and **cooling down**. So further back in time it must have been **smaller** and **hotter**. If you trace time back **far enough**, you get a **Big Bang**.

THE BIG BANG THEORY:
The universe started off **very hot** and **very dense** (perhaps as an **infinitely hot, infinitely dense** singularity) and has been **expanding** ever since.

If the universe began at a specific point in time, i.e. with the Big Bang, then it has a finite age.

1) According to the Big Bang theory, **before** the Big Bang, there was **no space or time** — space-time **began** with the Big Bang, (when time = 0 and the radius of the universe = 0) and has been expanding ever since.

2) The red shift of light from other galaxies isn't caused by them flying away from us through space — they are moving away from us because **space itself** is **expanding**. You'd see the same thing looking from anywhere else in the universe.

Cosmic Microwave Background Radiation is Evidence for the Big Bang

1) The Big Bang model predicts that loads of **gamma radiation** was produced in the **very early universe**. This radiation should **still** be observed today (it hasn't had anywhere else to go).

2) Because the universe has **expanded**, the wavelengths of this cosmic background radiation have been **stretched** and are now in the **microwave** region.

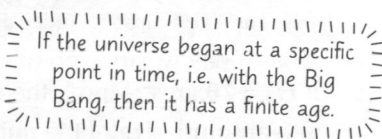

3) Cosmic microwave background radiation (CMBR) was picked up **accidentally** by Penzias and Wilson in the 1960s.

4) In the late 1980s a satellite called the **Cosmic Background Explorer** (**COBE**) was sent up to have a **detailed look** at the radiation. It found a **continuous spectrum** corresponding to a **temperature** of about **2.7 K**.

5) The radiation is largely the same everywhere (**homogeneous**) and in all directions (**isotropic**), in line with the **Cosmological principle**.

6) There are **very tiny fluctuations** in temperature, which were at the limit of COBE's detection. These are due to tiny energy-density variations in the early universe, and are needed for the initial '**seeding**' of a star or galaxy formation.

7) The background radiation also shows a **Doppler shift**, indicating the Earth's motion through space. It turns out that the **Milky Way** is rushing towards an unknown mass (the **Great Attractor**) at over a **million miles an hour**.

Practice Questions

Q1 What is the Cosmological principle?
Q2 Describe and explain the Doppler effect on waves. What observable effect does it have on EM waves?
Q3 State Hubble's law, in symbols and in words.
Q4 Give two units for measuring H_0.
Q5 Explain how the discovery of cosmic microwave background radiation supports the Big Bang theory.

Exam Questions

Q1 a) An astronomer observes that the spectral line corresponding to a wavelength of 650 nm has been shifted to 890 nm in the spectra from a distant object. Estimate the speed at which the object is moving, giving a direction. *(c = 3.00 × 10⁸ ms⁻¹)* [2 marks]

b) Use Hubble's law to estimate the distance (in light years) that the object is from us. (Use $H_0 = 2.4 \times 10^{-18}$ s⁻¹, 1 ly = 9.5 × 10¹⁵ m) [2 marks]

Q2 Explain why the red shift of light from other galaxies provides evidence for the Big Bang model of the universe. [3 marks]

So it's not just about socially awkward physicists trying to get a date then...
I love this stuff, but it's pretty bizarre trying to get your head around it, particularly the stuff about space-time expanding. Just take it nice and slow, and go back over it a few times to let it sink in.

The Evolution of the Universe

If you thought expanding space-time was weird, just wait till we get to dark energy...

The Age and Observable Size of the Universe Depend on H_0

1) If the universe has been **expanding** at the **same rate** for its whole life, the **age** of the universe is: $\boxed{t = H_0^{-1}}$
   This is only an estimate since the universe probably hasn't always been expanding at the same rate.

2) Unfortunately, since no one knows the **exact value** of H_0 we can only guess the universe's age.
   If $H_0 = 70$ kms^{-1}Mpc^{-1}, then the age of the universe $\approx 1/(2.2... \times 10^{-18}$ s$^{-1}) = 4.4... \times 10^{17}$ s = **14 billion years**.

3) The **absolute size** of the universe is **unknown** but there is a limit on the size of the **observable universe**.
   This is simply a **sphere** (with the Earth at its centre) with a **radius** equal to the **maximum distance** that **light**
   can travel during its **age**. So if $H_0 = 70$ kms^{-1}Mpc^{-1} then this sphere will have a radius of **14 billion light years**.
   Taking into account the **expansion** of the universe (p.36), it is thought to be more like 46-47 billion light years.

The Story So Far (as far as we know)...

Before 10^{-4} seconds after the Big Bang, this is mainly guesswork. There are plenty of theories around, but not much experimental evidence to back them up. The general consensus at the moment goes something like this:

1) **Big Bang to 10^{-43} seconds.** Well, it's anybody's guess, really. At this sort of size and energy, even
   general relativity stops working properly. This is the "infinitely hot, infinitely small, infinitely dense" bit.

2) **10^{-43} seconds to 10^{-4} seconds.** At the start of this period, there's no distinction between different types of
   force — there's just one grand unified force. Then the universe expands and cools, and the unified force
   splits into gravity, strong nuclear, weak nuclear and electromagnetic forces. Many cosmologists believe the
   universe went through a rapid period of expansion called inflation at about 10^{-34} s.

   The universe is a sea of quarks, antiquarks, leptons and photons. The quarks aren't bound up in particles
   like protons and neutrons, because there's too much energy around.

   At some point, matter-antimatter symmetry gets broken, so slightly more matter is made than antimatter.
   Nobody knows exactly how or when this happened, but most cosmologists like to put it as early as possible in the history of the universe.

Now we're onto more solid ground

3) **10^{-4} seconds.** This corresponds to a temperature of about 10^{12} K. The universe is cool enough for quarks
   to join up to form particles like protons and neutrons. They can never exist separately again. Matter and
   antimatter annihilate each other, leaving a small excess of matter and huge numbers of photons
   (resulting in the cosmic background radiation that we observe today).

4) **About 100 seconds.** Temperature has cooled to 10^9 K. The universe is similar to the interior of a star.
   Protons are cool enough to fuse to form helium nuclei.

5) **About 300 000 years.** Temperature has cooled to about 3000 K. The universe is cool enough for electrons
   (that were produced in the first millisecond) to combine with helium and hydrogen nuclei to form atoms.
   The universe becomes transparent since there are no free charges for the photons to interact with.
   This process is called recombination.

6) **About 14 billion years (now).** Temperature has cooled to about 2.7 K. Slight density fluctuations in the
   universe mean that, over time, clumps of matter have been condensed by gravity into galactic clusters,
   galaxies and individual stars.

Dark Matter Makes Things More Complicated

1) In the 1930s, the Swiss astronomer Fritz Zwicky calculated the mass of a **cluster of galaxies** (the COMA cluster)
   based on the **velocity** of its outer galaxies and compared this figure to the mass of the cluster as estimated from
   its **luminosity**. The mass calculated from the velocity was **much bigger**, suggesting there was 'extra' mass in the
   cluster that couldn't be **seen**.

2) In the 1970s, Vera Rubin observed that stars at the edges of **galaxies** were moving **faster** than they should given
   the mass and distribution of stars in the galaxy. For Newton's laws to hold, there needed to be **extra matter** in the
   galaxies that hadn't been accounted for.

3) These observations suggest there is something **extra** in the universe, giving mass to galaxies, that we **can't see**.

4) This theoretical substance has been called '**dark matter**'. Astrophysicists now estimate that there is about **five
   times** as much dark matter as ordinary matter in the universe, and that dark matter makes up about **25% of the
   universe** in total.

The Evolution of the Universe

No One Knows What Dark Matter Is

1) One explanation is that dark matter is made up of **MACHOs** (Massive Compact Halo Objects). These are objects made of **normal matter** in a very **dense** form, that don't give off light and so are hard to detect, e.g. **black holes** (p.31) and **brown dwarfs** (stars that aren't massive enough for nuclear fusion to take place). Astronomers looking for evidence of these kinds of objects have had **some success**, but it's **unlikely** that MACHOs made of normal matter account for **all the dark matter** in the universe, as this would require more protons and neutrons to exist than is compatible with our current understanding of the **Big Bang**.

2) Another idea is that dark matter is made of **WIMPs** (Weakly Interacting Massive Particles). These are exotic particles that don't interact with the **electromagnetic force**, but do interact with **gravity**. As yet, though, no particle like this has ever been detected, and WIMPs are currently **purely theoretical**.

3) There's also the possibility that dark matter **doesn't really exist at all**, and is an illusion caused by **mistakes** in other theories. But most scientists **agree that it is there**, even if we don't know what it is yet.

Dark Energy is making the Universe Expand More Quickly

1) Everything in the universe is attracted to everything else by **gravity**. This means the expansion of the universe should be **slowing down**.

2) Historically, astronomers debated whether this would slow the expansion of the universe enough to cause it to contract back in on itself (in a so called 'Big Crunch'), or if the universe would go on expanding forever.

3) In the late 1990s, astronomers discovered something entirely **unexpected**. Rather than slowing down, the expansion of the universe appears to be **accelerating**. Astronomers are trying to explain this acceleration using **dark energy** — a type of energy that fills the whole of space.

4) There are various theories of what this dark energy is, but it's really hard to test them. So like dark matter, it's currently a **mystery**.

Based on current observations, **dark energy** makes up about **70%** of the universe. As **dark matter** makes up another **25%**, this means that only about **5%** of the universe is made up of **ordinary matter**. Or to put it another way, we have very little idea what 95% of the universe is made up of.

Practice Questions

Q1 Using the Big Bang theory, describe the evolution of the universe from the beginning up to the present day.

Q2 Explain what is meant by the terms MACHOs and WIMPs.

Q3 What discovery led scientists to think that 70% of the universe is made up of dark energy?

Q4 What percentage of the universe is thought to be made up of ordinary matter?

Exam Questions

Q1 Assume $H_0 = 50$ kms^{-1}Mpc^{-1} (to 2 s.f.). *(1 year ≈ 3.16 × 10^7 s, 1 pc = 3.1 × 10^{16} m)*

a) Calculate H_0 in SI units. [2 marks]

b) Calculate an estimate of the age of the universe, and hence the radius of the observable universe, ignoring expansion. [3 marks]

Q2 Some scientists believe that weakly interacting massive particles (WIMPs) are a candidate for the dark matter which makes up around 25% of the universe. Explain why scientists believe dark matter must exist, and give a reason why it cannot be ordinary matter that emits little or no radiation. [4 marks]

So, this book only applies to about 5% of the universe?...

Dark matter and dark energy represent a huge hole in our knowledge — trying to understand the universe without studying them is like trying to revise for your exams by only learning 5% of the course (not a good idea, by the way). This stuff is a great example of how science works though — we have a theory, make some observations, find something that doesn't fit in with our predictions, then look for a new way of explaining it. Ach, science, don't you just love it?

Capacitors

Capacitors are things that store electrical charge — like a charge bucket. The capacitance of one of these things tells you how much charge the bucket can hold. Sounds simple enough... ha... ha, ha, ha...

Capacitors Build Up Charge on Plates

1) A **capacitor** is an electrical component that can **store electrical charge**.

2) Capacitors are made up of two **conducting plates** separated by a **gap** or a **dielectric** (an insulating material).

3) The **circuit symbol** for a capacitor is two **parallel lines**.

4) When a capacitor is connected to a **power source**, **positive** and **negative** charge build up on **opposite** plates. The insulating material (which could be an **air gap**) stops charge moving between the two plates, so a **potential difference** is created.

5) This creates a **uniform electric field** (p.47) between the plates.

Remember, the potential difference between two points is the work done in moving a unit charge between them.

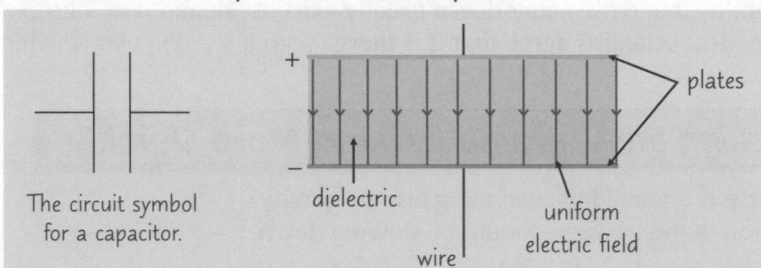

The circuit symbol for a capacitor.   dielectric   uniform electric field   plates   wire

6) The amount of **charge per unit voltage** stored by a capacitor is called its **capacitance**.

$$C = \frac{Q}{V}$$

where Q is the charge in coulombs, V is the potential difference in volts and C is the capacitance in farads (F) — 1 farad = 1 C V^{-1}.

7) A farad is a **huge** unit so you'll usually see capacitances expressed in terms of:

μF — microfarads ($\times 10^{-6}$)   **nF** — nanofarads ($\times 10^{-9}$)   **pF** — picofarads ($\times 10^{-12}$)

Combined Capacitance Increases in Parallel, but Decreases in Series

Depending on how you place **capacitors** in a **circuit**, you can increase or decrease the amount of **charge stored**.

You could be asked to solve circuit problems using these equations.

If you put two or more **capacitors** in a **parallel circuit**, the **potential difference** across each one is the **same**.

Each capacitor can store the **same** amount of **charge** as it would if it was the **only component** in the circuit.

So, the **total capacitance** is just the **sum** of the individual capacitances:

$$C_{total} = C_1 + C_2$$

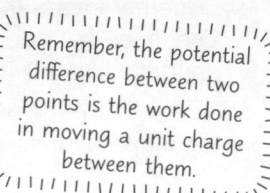

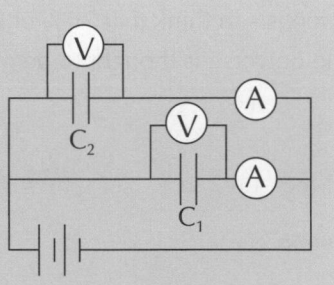

When you put capacitors in a **series circuit**, the **potential difference** is **shared** between them.

Each capacitor stores the **same charge**. It can be shown that:

$$\frac{1}{C_{total}} = \frac{1}{C_1} + \frac{1}{C_2} + \frac{1}{C_3}$$

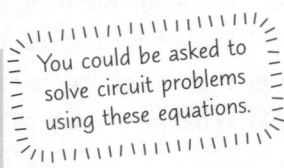

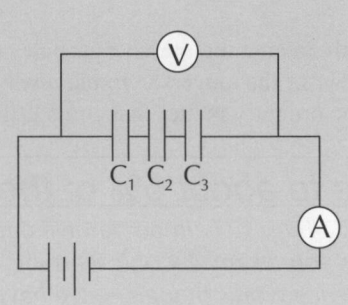

You can keep adding as many capacitors you want like this — the formula will just be:
$$\frac{1}{C_{total}} = \frac{1}{C_1} + \frac{1}{C_2} + \frac{1}{C_3} + \frac{1}{C_4} + ...$$

Capacitors

You Can **Investigate Capacitors** in **Series** and **Parallel**

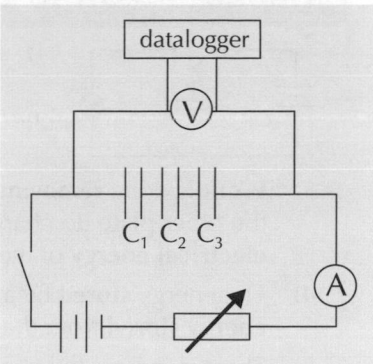

1) Set up a **test series circuit** to measure current and potential difference. Add a **variable resistor** and a switch. Close the switch.

2) Constantly adjust the **variable resistor** to keep the charging current **constant** for as long as you can (it's impossible when the capacitor is nearly fully charged).

3) A **data logger** connected to the **voltmeter** can be used to record the **potential difference** over **time**. Once the capacitors are fully charged, open the **switch**.

4) Rearrange the circuit so the capacitors are in **parallel** (like the diagram on the previous page, but now with a variable resistor). Make sure they have been discharged first (see p.43). Close the switch and repeat step 2.

5) Once both circuits have been tested, you can plot graphs of **current against time** and **charge against potential difference** (using $\Delta Q = I\Delta t$).

Assuming all three capacitors have the same **capacitance** C, and can hold a **charge** of Q, your graphs will look like:

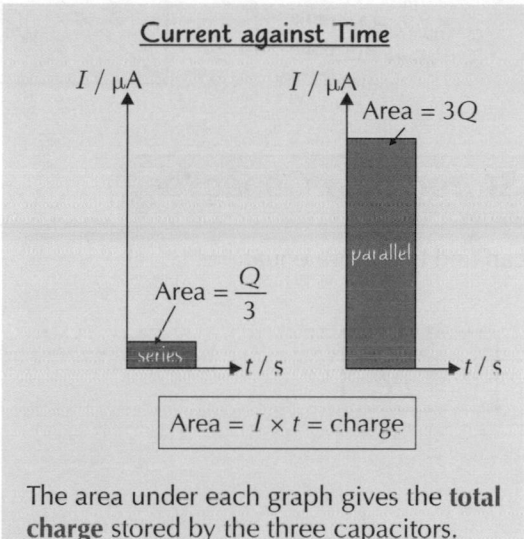

The area under each graph gives the **total charge** stored by the three capacitors.

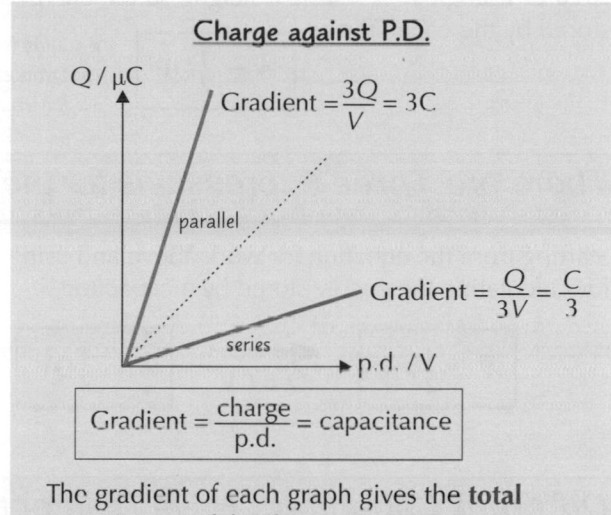

The gradient of each graph gives the **total capacitance** of the three capacitors.

Practice Questions

Q1 What is a capacitor?

Q2 Define capacitance and write down the formula for calculating it.

Q3 How do you find the total capacitance of a circuit if the capacitors are placed in parallel?

Q4 Describe an experiment you could do to show how capacitance changes for a parallel and series circuit.

Exam Questions

Q1 From the graphs shown on the right, calculate the capacitance of the capacitor and the charge stored on its plates after 66 seconds.

[4 marks]

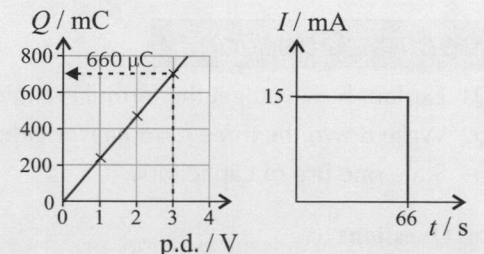

Q2 a) Two capacitors are connected in series and a potential difference of 12 V is applied to them. Calculate the total charge stored in the circuit. The capacitance of the first capacitor is 12 pF and for the second is 7.0 pF.

[2 marks]

b) The same potential difference is applied but now the capacitors are connected in parallel. Calculate the new total charge stored in the circuit.

[2 marks]

Capacitance — fun, it's not...

Capacitors are really useful in the real world. Pick an appliance, any appliance, and it'll probably have a capacitor or several. If I'm being honest, though, the only saving grace of these pages for me is that they're not especially hard...

Energy Stored by Capacitors

Capacitors are handy for storing small amounts of energy that can be accessed quickly.

Capacitors **Store Energy**

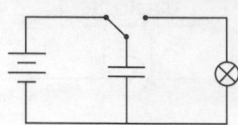

1) In this circuit, when the switch is flicked to the **left**, charge builds up on the plates of the **capacitor**. **Electrical energy**, provided by the battery, is **stored** by the capacitor.

2) If the switch is flicked to the **right**, the energy stored on the plates will **discharge** through the **bulb**, converting electrical energy into light and heat.

3) **Work** is done **removing negative charge** from **one plate** and depositing it onto the other plate (to charge the capacitor). The energy for this must come from the **electrical energy** of the **battery**, and is given by **charge × average p.d.**

4) The energy **stored** by a capacitor is **equal** to the **work done** by the **battery**. So, you can find the **energy stored** from the **area** under a **graph** of **p.d.** against **charge stored** on the capacitor.

5) The p.d. across the capacitor is **proportional** to the charge stored on it, so the graph will be a **straight line** through the origin. The **energy stored** is given by the **yellow triangle**.

Area of triangle = ½ × base × height, so the energy stored by the capacitor is:

$$W = \frac{1}{2}QV$$

W stands for 'work done', but you can also use E for 'energy stored'.

You need to remember where this equation comes from.

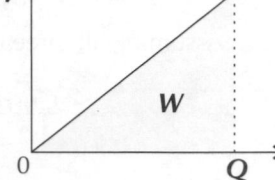

There are **Three** Expressions for the **Energy Stored** by a Capacitor

Starting from the equation for work above and using $C = \frac{Q}{V}$ you can find two more equations for calculating the energy stored by a capacitor:

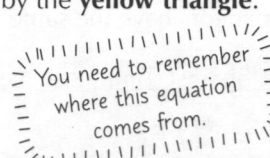

$$W = \frac{1}{2}V^2C \quad \xleftarrow{\;Q = CV\;} \quad W = \frac{1}{2}QV \quad \xrightarrow{\;V = \frac{Q}{C}\;} \quad W = \frac{1}{2}\frac{Q^2}{C}$$

Different Capacitors Have Different **Uses**

Capacitors are found in loads of **electronic devices**. They don't store much charge, so can't replace **batteries**, but they can discharge **quicker** than batteries, which makes them very useful. What's more, the **amount of charge** that can be stored and the **rate** at which it's **released** can be controlled by the capacitor chosen. Some uses for them are:

1) **Flash photography** — when you take a picture, the capacitor has to discharge really quickly to give a **short pulse** of high current to create a brief, bright flash.

2) **Back-up power supplies** — these often use lots of large capacitors that can release charge for a **short period** if the power supply goes off — e.g. for keeping computer systems running if there's a brief power outage.

3) **Smoothing out p.d.** — when converting an **a.c. power** supply to **d.c. power**, capacitors charge up during the **peaks** and discharge during the **troughs**, helping to maintain a **constant output**.

Practice Questions

Q1 Explain how you get the formula relating work, charge and voltage for a capacitor.

Q2 Write down the three formulas for calculating the energy stored by a capacitor.

Q3 State one use of capacitors.

Exam Questions

Q1 Calculate the energy stored by a capacitor if it is charged from a 12 V source and holds a charge of 0.6 nC. [1 mark]

Q2 Calculate the capacitance of a capacitor that stores 2.5×10^{-10} J of energy if it is charged from a 5 V supply. [1 mark]

Short and sweet — just how I like my physics...

Make sure you can explain how to get the energy equations as well as how to use them and you're pretty much sorted.

Charging and Discharging

Charging and discharging — sounds painful...

You can **Investigate** what Happens when you **Charge** a **Capacitor**

1) Set up the test circuit shown in the circuit diagram.

2) Close the switch to connect the **uncharged** capacitor to the power supply.

3) Let the capacitor **charge** whilst the **data logger** records both the **potential difference** (from the voltmeter) and the **current** (from the ammeter) over time.

4) When the current through the ammeter is **zero**, the capacitor is fully charged.

5) You can then use a computer to plot a graph of **charge**, **p.d.** or **current against time**, as shown below (remember $\Delta Q = I\Delta t$).

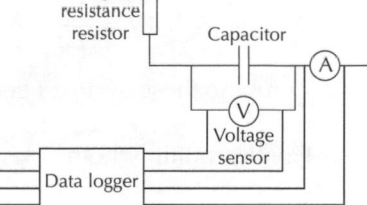

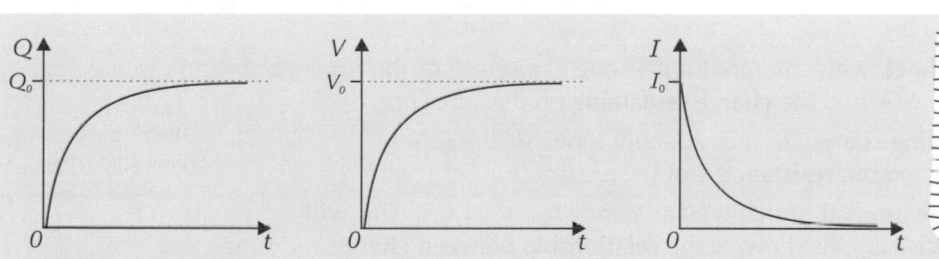

These circuits charge and discharge capacitors through a fixed resistor. You'll see on p.45 that resistance slows down the charge/discharge. In practice, using a resistor makes the process slower and easier to investigate.

1) As soon as the switch closes, current starts to flow. The electrons flow onto the plate connected to the **negative terminal** of the power supply, so a **negative charge** builds up.

2) This build-up of negative charge **repels electrons** off the plate connected to the **positive terminal** of the power supply, making that plate positive. These electrons are attracted to the positive terminal of the power supply.

3) An **equal** but **opposite** charge builds up on each plate, causing a **potential difference** between the plates. Remember that **no charge** can flow **between** the plates because they're **separated** by an **insulator** (gap or dielectric).

4) Initially the **current** through the circuit is **high**. But, as **charge** builds up on the plates, **electrostatic repulsion** makes it **harder** and **harder** for more electrons to be deposited. When the p.d. across the **capacitor** is equal to the p.d. across the **power supply**, the **current** falls to zero. The capacitor is **fully charged**.

An equal but opposite charge

To **Discharge** a **Capacitor**, **Disconnect** the **Power** and **Reconnect** the **Circuit**

1) **Disconnect** the power supply from the test circuit above, reconnect the circuit and close the **switch**.

2) Let the capacitor **discharge** whilst the data logger records **potential difference** and **current** over time.

3) When the **current** through the ammeter and the **potential difference** across the plates fall to **zero**, the capacitor is fully discharged.

4) You can once more plot **graphs** of **p.d.**, **charge** and **current** against **time**:

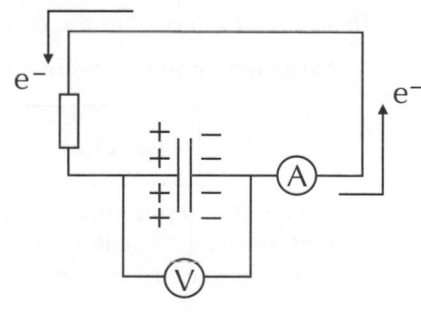

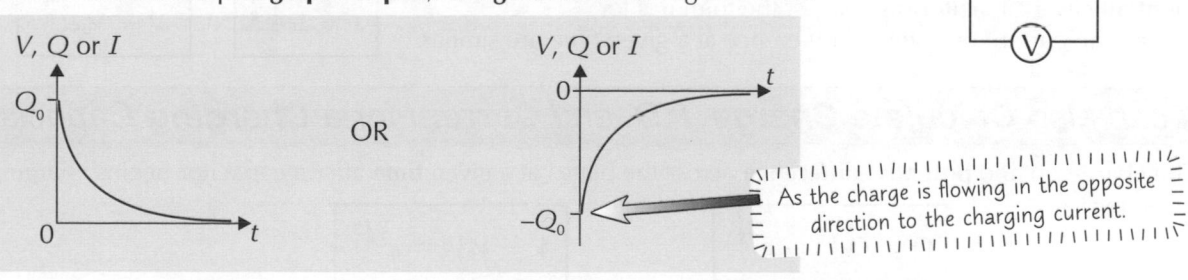

OR

As the charge is flowing in the opposite direction to the charging current.

The electrons (current) flow from the **negative** plate to the **positive** plate (shown above).
Initially, the current is **high**, but as the charge leaves the plates, the **potential difference** across the plates **decreases**. So the **electrostatic repulsion** decreases, reducing the flow of current.

Charging and Discharging

You Can **Model Discharging** Capacitors with a **Spreadsheet**

You can predict **roughly** how the stored **charge** will **change over time** for any **discharging** capacitor with capacitance C and initial charge Q, in a circuit with resistance R. You need to find the change in charge over a **tiny time interval** and **repeat** this process for a long period of time. To do this, you'll need an equation which relates ΔQ and Δt.

You know that $I = \dfrac{\Delta Q}{\Delta t}$ and also that $I = \dfrac{V}{R}$, so $\dfrac{\Delta Q}{\Delta t} = \dfrac{V}{R}$. For capacitors, $Q = CV$ so $V = \dfrac{Q}{C}$.

Combine these and you get $\dfrac{\Delta Q}{\Delta t} = -\dfrac{Q}{RC}$. There's a minus sign here because the charge is decreasing over time.

Finally, multiply both sides by Δt to get $\Delta Q = -\dfrac{Q}{RC}\Delta t$.

Spreadsheet Modelling

1) Create a new **spreadsheet**, with columns for the **time** elapsed since the capacitor began discharging, t, the **change in charge**, ΔQ, and the **charge remaining** on the capacitor, Q.

2) Choose an **initial starting charge** for the capacitor along with a value for the **capacitance** C and the **resistance** R of the resistor.

There's more on modelling exponential relationships with spreadsheets on p.73.

3) Choose a sensible **time interval** Δt that is significantly less than CR. This will let you plot more **precise** graphs showing the **relationship** between **charge** and **time**.

4) In the initial row, $t_0 = 0$ and $Q_0 = $ initial charge. Leave ΔQ blank in this row.

5) In the next row:
   - The **new time** $t_1 = t_0 + \Delta t$.
   - You can write a formula for the **change in charge**, ΔQ, over the time interval by using the equation $\Delta Q = -\dfrac{Q}{RC}\Delta t$ above. I'll call it $(\Delta Q)_1$.
   - The **new charge** is given by $Q_1 = Q_0 + (\Delta Q)_1$ so write a formula for that too.

6) **Repeat** this process of calculating the values in each row from Q and t in the **row above**. If you write the formulas correctly, you can use the spreadsheet program to **automatically fill** in as many rows as you want.

7) Once you have enough points, plot a **graph** of **charge** against **time**. It should be similar to the graph for a **discharging capacitor** shown on page 43.

The **Charge** on a Discharging Capacitor **Decreases Exponentially**

The **shape** of the graph you plot from the model above is actually one of **exponential decay** (p.88). This means that when a capacitor is **discharging**, the amount of **charge** left on the plates falls **exponentially with time**.

It always takes the **same length of time** for the charge to **halve**, no matter **how much charge** you start with — like radioactive decay (see p.74-75).

In fact, for a given **proportion**, it always takes the same time for that proportion of the charge to be lost — it's known as the **constant ratio property** of exponential relationships.

See p.43 for the graphs showing the exponential relationships of Q, V and I.

The **charge** left on the plates of a capacitor discharging from full is given by the equation:

$$Q = Q_0 e^{\frac{-t}{CR}}$$

where Q_0 is the charge of the capacitor when it's fully charged (C), t is time since discharging began (s), R is the resistance (Ω) and C is the capacitance (F).

As the **current** and **potential difference** also decrease **exponentially** as a capacitor discharges, the formulas for calculating the current or potential difference at a given time are similar:

$$I = I_0 e^{\frac{-t}{CR}} \qquad V = V_0 e^{\frac{-t}{CR}}$$

You can also **Calculate Charge**, **P.D.** and **Current** for a **Charging** Capacitor

1) The **charge** on and **potential difference** across the plates at a given **time** after a capacitor begins charging are given by:

$$Q = Q_0(1 - e^{\frac{-t}{CR}}) \qquad V = V_0(1 - e^{\frac{-t}{CR}})$$

2) The **charging current decreases exponentially** (it just travels in the **opposite direction** to the discharging current). So the formula for the charging current at a given time is the **same** as for a **discharging** capacitor:

$$I = I_0 e^{\frac{-t}{CR}}$$

Charging and Discharging

The Time Taken to Charge or Discharge Depends on Two Factors

The **time** it takes to charge up or discharge a capacitor depends on:

1) The **capacitance** of the capacitor (**C**). This affects the amount of **charge** that can be transferred at a given **voltage**.

2) The **resistance** of the circuit (**R**). This affects the **current** in the circuit.

Time Constant $\tau = CR$ τ is the Greek letter 'tau'

If $t = \tau = CR$ is put into the equation for the charge on a discharging capacitor, then $Q = Q_0 e^{-1}$.

So when $t = \tau$: $\dfrac{Q}{Q_0} = \dfrac{1}{e} \approx \dfrac{1}{2.718} \approx 0.37$.

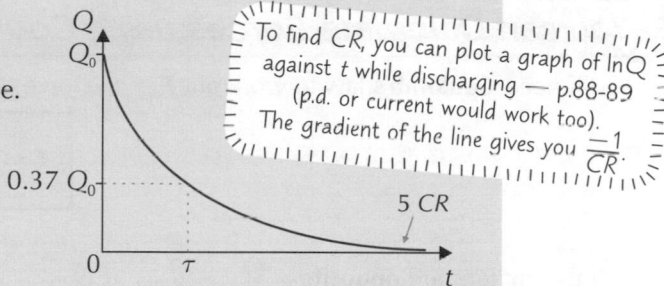

To find CR, you can plot a graph of $\ln Q$ against t while discharging — p.88-89 (p.d. or current would work too). The gradient of the line gives you $\dfrac{-1}{CR}$.

1) So τ, the **time constant**, is the time taken for the **charge**, **potential difference** or **current** on a discharging capacitor to **fall** to **37%** of its initial value.

2) It's also the time taken for the **charge** or **potential difference** of a **charging** capacitor to **rise** to **63%** of it's maximum value.

3) The **larger** the **resistor** in series with the capacitor, the **longer it takes** to charge or discharge.

4) In practice, the time taken for a capacitor to charge or discharge **fully** is taken to be about 5CR.

τ can be found experimentally by using a voltmeter and timing how long it takes a discharging capacitor to reach 37% of its starting potential difference.

Practice Questions

Q1 Describe an experiment you could do to investigate how charge changes over time for a charging capacitor.

Q2 Sketch graphs to show how the p.d. across the plates of a capacitor changes with time for:
a) charging a capacitor,   b) discharging a capacitor,
and explain what effect the p.d. has on the current, in terms of electron flow.

Q3 Describe how you could model the change of charge across a discharging capacitor with a spreadsheet.

Q4 Describe what effect the initial charge on a capacitor has on the time taken for the charge to half.

Q5 State the formula for calculating the p.d. across a charging capacitor at a time t after charging began.

Q6 What two factors affect the rate of charge of a capacitor?

Q7 What is meant by the 'time constant' of a capacitor and how could you find it from a graph of $\ln Q$ against t?

Exam Question

Q1 A 250 µF capacitor is fully charged from a 6 V battery and then discharged through a 1 kΩ resistor.

a) Calculate the time taken for the charge on the capacitor to fall to 37% of its original value. [2 marks]

b) Calculate the percentage of the initial charge remaining on the capacitor after 0.7s. [2 marks]

c) If the charging voltage is increased to 12 V, what effect will this have on:

i) the total charge stored, [1 mark]

ii) the capacitance of the capacitor, [1 mark]

iii) the time taken to fully charge. [1 mark]

An analogy — consider the lowly bike pump...

A good way to think of the charging process is like pumping air into a bike tyre. To start with, the air goes in easily, but as the pressure in the tyre increases, it gets harder and harder to squeeze any more air in. The tyre's 'full' when the pressure of the air in the tyre equals the pressure of the pump. The analogy works just as well for discharging...

Electric Fields

*Electric fields can be attractive or repulsive, so they're different from gravitational ones. It's all to do with **charge**.*

There is an **Electric Field** around a **Charged Object**

Any object with **charge** has an **electric field** around it — the region where it can attract or repel other charges.

1) Electric charge, **Q**, is measured in **coulombs** (C) and can be either positive or negative.
2) **Oppositely** charged particles **attract** each other. **Like** charges **repel**.
3) If a **charged object** is placed in an electric field, then it will experience a **force**.
4) If the charged object is a **sphere**, and the charge is evenly distributed (it's spherically symmetrical), you can assume all of its **charge** is at its **centre**.
5) Just like with gravitational fields, **electric fields** can be represented by **field lines**.

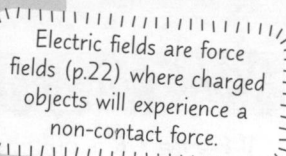
Electric fields are force fields (p.22) where charged objects will experience a non-contact force.

You can **Calculate Forces** using **Coulomb's Law**

You'll need **Coulomb's law** to work out **F** — the force of attraction or repulsion between two point charges.

$$F = \frac{Qq}{4\pi\varepsilon_0 r^2}$$

ε_0 ("epsilon-nought") is the permittivity of free space,
Q and q are the charges,
r is the distance between Q and q.

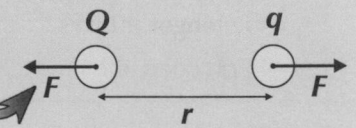

If the charges are **opposite** then the force is **attractive**. **F** will be **negative**.

If **Q** and **q** are **like** charges then the force is **repulsive**, and **F** will be **positive**.

1) The force on Q is always **equal** and **opposite** to the force on q.
2) It's an **inverse square law** (again — see p.22). The further apart the charges are, the weaker the force between them.
3) The size of the **force** F also depends on the **permittivity**, ε, of the **material** between the two charges. For **free space** (a vacuum), the permittivity is $\varepsilon_0 = 8.85 \times 10^{-12}$ $C^2N^{-1}m^{-2}$.

You can also give the units as Fm^{-1}.

Electric Field Strength is Force per Unit Charge

Electric field strength, **E**, is defined as the **force per unit positive charge** — the force that a charge of +1 C would experience if it was placed in the electric field.

$$E = \frac{F}{Q}$$

1) **E** is a **vector** pointing in the **direction** that a **positive charge** would **move**.
2) The units of E are **newtons per coulomb** (NC⁻¹).
3) Field strength depends on **where you are** in the field.
4) A **point charge** — or any body which behaves as if all its charge is concentrated at the centre — has a **radial** field.

F is the force acting on a charge Q which is in the electric field. Here, Q is not causing the electric field. Don't confuse it with the Q in the section below.

In a **Radial Field, E** is **Inversely Proportional** to r^2

1) When the electric field is being generated by a **point charge**, we call the charge generating the field **Q** and **redefine** the charge experiencing the **force** as **q**. In a **radial field**, E depends on the **distance** r from the point charge Q.

$$E = \frac{Q}{4\pi\varepsilon_0 r^2}$$

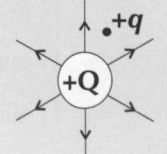
For a **positive** Q, the small positive 'test' charge q would be repelled, so the field lines point away from Q.

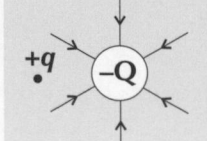
For a **negative** Q, the small positive charge q would be attracted, so the field lines point towards Q.

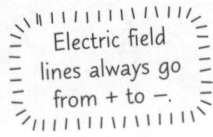
Electric field lines always go from + to −.

2) It's another **inverse square law** — $E \propto \frac{1}{r^2}$

3) Field strength **decreases** as you go **further away** from Q — on a diagram, the **field lines** get **further apart**.

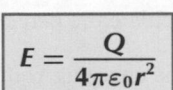

The area under the graph is the electric potential, p.48.

Electric Fields

Field Strength is the Same Everywhere in a Uniform Field

A **uniform field** can be produced by connecting two **parallel plates** to the opposite poles of a battery.

1) **Field strength** E is the **same** at **all points** between the two plates and is given by:

$$E = \frac{V}{d}$$

V is the potential difference between the plates, d is the distance between them.

2) E can also be measured in volts per metre (Vm^{-1}).

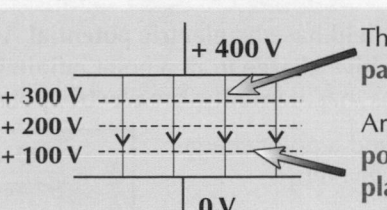

+ 400 V
+ 300 V
+ 200 V
+ 100 V
0 V

The **field lines** are **parallel** to each other.

Areas with the **same potential** are **parallel** to the plates, and **perpendicular** to the **field lines**.

Parallel Plate Capacitors Generate a Uniform Field

C is measured in farads (F). This is a large unit though, so you'll often see nano- or picofarad capacitors.

1) The **capacitance** (p.40) of a capacitor depends on how easy it is to generate an **electric field** between its two plates.

2) It also depends on the **dimensions** of the capacitor, and can be calculated by using:

$$C = \frac{\varepsilon_0 A}{d}$$

Where A is the area of the plates (m^2), ε_0 is the permittivity of free space (Fm^{-1}), and d is the separation of the plates (m).

3) If the plates have a **material** in between them instead of a **vacuum**, ε_0 is replaced with **permittivity**, ε, where:

$$\varepsilon = \varepsilon_r \varepsilon_0$$

Where ε_r is the relative permittivity (a ratio of the size of the electric field generated in a vacuum, compared to if it was generated in a material).

Charged Particles Move Through Uniform Electric Fields Like Projectiles

You'll probably remember that **projectiles** move through a **uniform gravitational field** along a curved path (you met this in year 1 of A-level). **Charged particles** do a similar thing when they move through **uniform electric fields**.

1) A particle of charge Q will experience a **constant force**, given by $F = EQ$, acting **parallel** to the **electric field lines**.

2) If the particle is **positively charged** then the force is in the **same direction** as the field lines. If it's **negatively charged** (e.g. an **electron**), the force is in the **opposite direction** to the field lines.

3) The **work done** on the particle by this force ($W = Fd$) increases its **kinetic energy** and causes it to **accelerate at a constant rate** in the direction of the force (**Newton's second law**).

4) If the particle's **velocity** has a **component** at **right angles** to the field lines, this **component** will remain **unchanged** and the **velocity** in **this direction** will be **uniform**. That's **Newton's first law**.

5) The combined effect of constant acceleration and constant velocity at right angles to one another is a **curved path**.

Practice Questions

Q1 Describe the force field that surrounds a positively charged sphere with evenly distributed charge. State the assumption made.

Q2 Write down Coulomb's law.

Q3 Define electric field strength. Write an equation for the electric field strength of any electric field.

Q4 Describe the path a charged particle would take as it travels at an angle through a uniform electric field.

Exam Questions

Q1 The diagram shows two electric charges with equal but opposite charge, Q. Draw electric field lines to show the electric field in the area surrounding the charges.   •$+Q$ •$-Q$ [3 marks]

Q2 Find the electric field strength at a distance of 1.75×10^{-10} m from a 1.60×10^{-19} C point charge.   [2 marks]

Q3 Two parallel plates are separated by an air gap of 4.5 mm. The plates are connected to a 1500 V dc supply. Calculate the electric field strength between the plates. State the direction of the field.   [2 marks]

Q4 A parallel plate capacitor, P, has square plates of side length 5.0 mm which are separated by a gap of 2.0 mm. This gap is fully filled by a material with a relative permittivity of 4.1. Calculate the capacitance of P.   [3 marks]

Electric fields — one way to roast beef...

At least you get a choice here — uniform or radial, positive or negative, attractive or repulsive, chocolate or strawberry...

Electric Potential

Electric potential is all to do with how much energy a charge has based on where it is in an electric field.

Electric Potential is Potential Energy per Unit Charge

All points in an **electric field** have an **electric potential**, **V**. This is equal to the **work done** bringing a **unit positive charge** from a point **infinitely** far away to that point in the electric field. This means that at **infinity**, the **electric potential** will be **zero**.

In a **radial field** around a point charge, **electric potential** is given by:

$$V = \frac{Q}{4\pi\varepsilon_0 r}$$

where V is electric potential (V),
Q is the size of the point charge (C)
and r is the distance from the point charge (m).

1) The **sign** of **V** depends on the charge Q — i.e. V is **positive** when Q is **positive** and the force is **repulsive** (when acting on a unit positive charge), and **negative** when Q is negative and the force is **attractive**.

2) The **absolute magnitude** of V is **greatest** on the **surface of the charge**, and **decreases** as the **distance** from the charge **increases.**

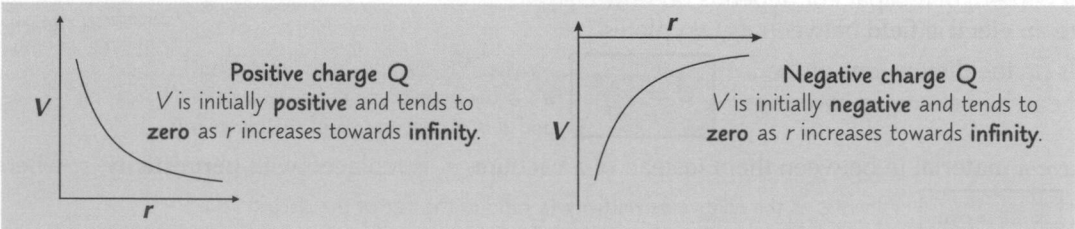

Positive charge Q
V is initially **positive** and tends to **zero** as r increases towards **infinity**.

Negative charge Q
V is initially **negative** and tends to **zero** as r increases towards **infinity**.

If you **move** a unit charge and **change** its **electric potential**, you have to apply a **force** and do **work**. For a point charge (and therefore also for a spherical charge, see p.46) you can plot the **force** applied, **F**, **against** the **distance**, **r**, from the charge producing the **electric field**.

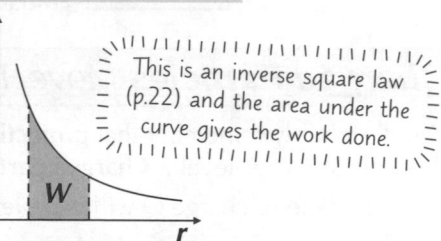

This is an inverse square law (p.22) and the area under the curve gives the work done.

From Electric Potential you can find Electric Potential Energy...

Electric potential is the **electric potential energy** that a **unit positive charge** (+1 C) would have at a certain point. This means you can find the electric potential energy for **any charge** at that point in the electric field by multiplying the **electric potential** by the **value** of the charge.

$$E = Vq$$

$$E = \frac{Qq}{4\pi\varepsilon_0 r}$$

where E is the electric potential energy (J),
V is electric potential (V),
and q is the size of the charge in the electric field (C).

Don't confuse this E with the E for electric field strength on p.46.

... And Capacitance

You can use the formula for the **electric potential** of a **radial** field and the fact that $Q = CV$ (p.40) for capacitors to **derive** an expression for the **capacitance** of an **isolated charged sphere**, assuming the charge is evenly distributed.

1) As it is a charged sphere, you can assume all of its charge is at its **centre** and treat it like a **point charge.**

2) Substitute $V = \frac{Q}{C}$ into $V = \frac{Q}{4\pi\varepsilon_0 R} \longrightarrow \frac{Q}{C} = \frac{Q}{4\pi\varepsilon_0 R}$

Here, R is the radius of the sphere.

3) Cancel out the Q's: $\frac{1}{C} = \frac{1}{4\pi\varepsilon_0 R}$

4) Rearrange for C, which gives: $\boxed{C = 4\pi\varepsilon_0 R}$

The unit for C is farads.

Electric Potential

There are Similarities between Gravitational and Electric Fields...

If a lot of the stuff on the previous couple of pages sounded strangely familiar it could be because it's very similar to the stuff on gravitational fields (or it could be because you've learnt it before — this is a revision book after all).

Anyway, there are **four** big **similarities** between **electric** and **gravitational fields** that you need to know — read on.

Gravitational field strength, g, is **force** per **unit mass**.	Electric field strength, E, is **force** per **unit positive charge**.
Newton's law of gravitation for the **force** between two point masses is an **inverse square law**.	Coulomb's law for the electric **force** between two point charges is also an **inverse square law**.
The **field lines** for a spherical mass...	The **field lines** for a **negative** spherically symmetric charge...
Gravitational potential, V, is **potential energy** per **unit mass** and is **zero** at **infinity**.	Electric potential, V, is **potential energy** per **unit positive charge** and is **zero** at **infinity**.

... and Three Differences too

Gravitational and electric fields aren't all the same — you need to know the **three main differences**:

1) Gravitational forces are always **attractive**. Electric forces can be either **attractive** or **repulsive**.

2) Objects can be **shielded** from **electric** fields, but not from gravitational fields.

3) The size of an **electric force** depends on the **medium** between the charges, e.g. plastic or air. For gravitational forces, this makes no difference.

Practice Questions

Q1 What is meant by 'electric potential'?

Q2 State the formula for finding the electric potential in a radial field.

Q3 Sketch a graph of force against distance for a unit charge being moved out of a radial electric field. How would you calculate work done from the graph?

Q4 Derive the equation for the capacitance of an isolated charged sphere.

Exam Questions

$e = 1.60 \times 10^{-19}$ C, $\varepsilon_0 = 8.85 \times 10^{-12}$ C^{2}N^{-1}m^{-2} (Fm^{-1})

Q1 Point A is 1.00 mm away from an electron.

    a) Calculate the electric potential at point A.   **[2 marks]**

    b) A positron has an equal but opposite charge to an electron. A positron is placed at point A. Calculate the electric potential energy of the positron.   **[1 mark]**

    c) The positron is then placed at a point B, where the electric potential is -1.0×10^{-6} V. Calculate the distance from the electron to point B.   **[2 marks]**

Q2 Calculate the capacitance of an isolated sphere which has a diameter of 10.0 cm.   **[1 mark]**

Q3 State two similarities and one difference between gravitational and electric fields.   **[3 marks]**

I prefer gravitational fields — electric fields are repulsive...

Revising fields is a bit like a buy-one-get-one-free sale — you learn all about gravitational fields and they throw electric fields in for free. You just have to remember to change your ms for Qs and your Gs for $1/4\pi\varepsilon_0$s... okay, so it's not quite a BOGOF sale. Maybe more like a buy-one-get-one-half-price sale... anyway, you get the point — go learn some stuff.

Magnetic Fields

Magnetic fields — making pretty patterns with iron filings before spending an age trying to pick them off the magnet.

A **Magnetic Field** is a **Region** Where a **Force** is Exerted on **Magnetic Materials**

Magnetic fields exist around **permanent magnets** and **moving charges**.

1) Magnetic fields can be represented (mapped) by **field lines**.
2) Field lines go from **north** to **south**.
3) The **closer** the lines, the **stronger** the field.
   If the field lines are **equally spaced** and **in the same direction** the field is uniform (i.e. the same everywhere).

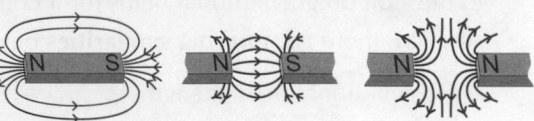

There is a **Magnetic Field** Around a **Wire** Carrying **Electric Current**

When **current** flows in any conductor, there's a **magnetic field** around the conductor. For a long straight wire:

1) The **field lines** are **concentric circles** centred on the wire.
2) The **direction** of the field can be worked out with the **right-hand rule**.
3) You also need to know the fields formed around **flat coils** and **solenoids**:

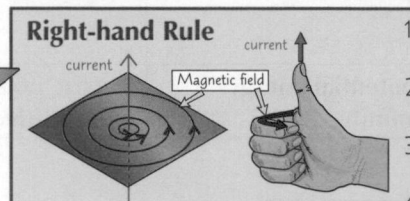

Right-hand Rule

1) Stick your right thumb up, like you're hitching a lift.
2) Your thumb points in the direction of conventional current...
3) ...and your curled fingers point in the direction of the field.
4) This also works for a flat coil.

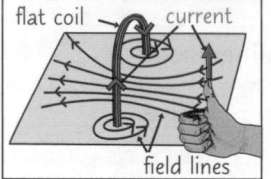

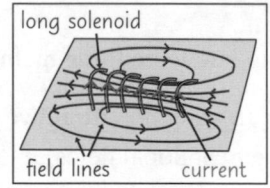

In each case, there's a sort of 'ring doughnut' field around the coil and a strong field inside it.

Learn these types of coil:

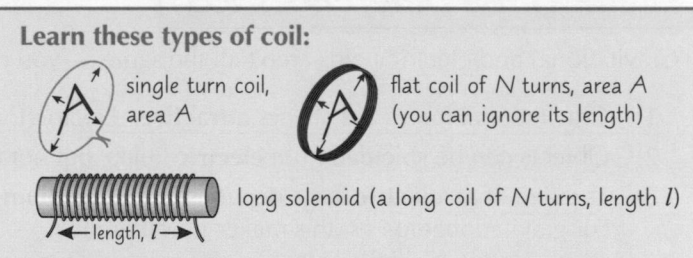

single turn coil, area *A*

flat coil of *N* turns, area *A* (you can ignore its length)

long solenoid (a long coil of *N* turns, length *l*)

A **Current Perpendicular** to a Uniform **Magnetic Field** will **Induce** a **Force**

For a current in a conductor that's **perpendicular** to the field lines in a **uniform** magnetic field:

1) The field around the wire and the external magnetic field will interact causing a **force** on the wire.
2) The **direction** of the force is always **perpendicular** to both the **current** direction and the **magnetic field** — it's given by **Fleming's left hand rule**...

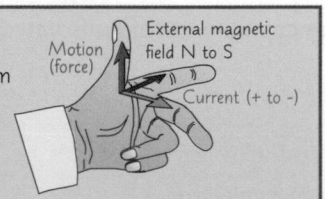

Fleming's Left Hand Rule
The First finger points in the direction of the external uniform magnetic Field, the seCond finger points in the direction of the conventional Current. Then your thuMb points in the direction of the force (in which Motion takes place).

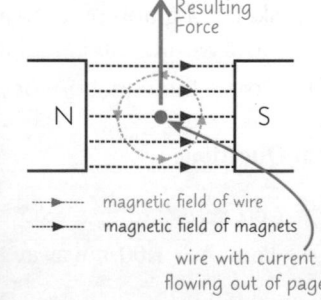

Resulting Force

N   S

- - - - ▶ magnetic field of wire
- - - - ▶ magnetic field of magnets
wire with current flowing out of page

The **Force** on a Conductor is **Proportional** to **Flux Density**

1) The size of the **force** on a **current-carrying** conductor at a **right angle** to an external magnetic field is proportional to the **magnetic flux density**, *B*. Magnetic flux density is used as a measure of the **strength** of a magnetic field.

2) **Magnetic flux density**, *B*, is **defined** as:

> The **force** on **one metre** of wire carrying a **current** of **one amp** at **right angles** to the **magnetic field**.

3) When current is at 90° to the magnetic field, the size of the **force**, *F* is proportional to the **current**, *I*, the **length of wire** in the field, *l*, as well as the **flux density**, *B*. This gives the equation: $\quad F = BIl$

4) **Flux density** is a **vector** quantity with both a **direction** and **magnitude**. It's measured in **teslas**, **T**: $\quad 1 \text{ tesla} = \dfrac{\text{Wb}}{\text{m}^2}$ ← It helps to think of flux density as the number of field lines (measured in webers (Wb), see p.54) per unit area.

Magnetic Fields

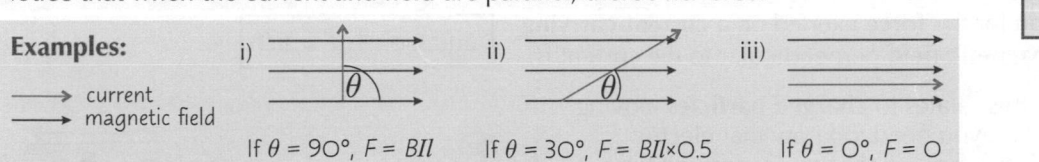

1) The **force** on a current-carrying wire in a magnetic field is caused by the **component** of the magnetic field which is **perpendicular** to the wire — *B* sin *θ*.

2) So, for a wire at an **angle** *θ* to the field, the **force** acting on the wire is given by: Notice that when the current and field are parallel, there's no force.

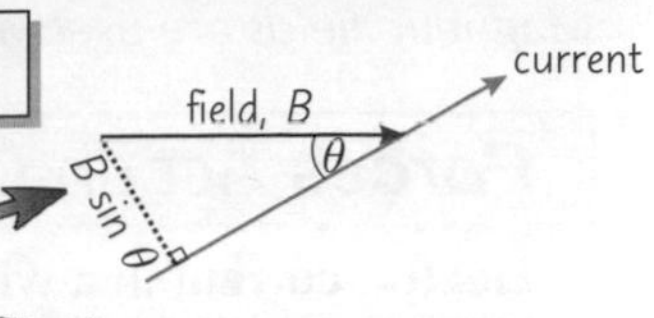

$$F = BIl \sin\theta$$

Examples:

→ current
→ magnetic field

i) *θ*
ii) *θ*
iii)

If *θ* = 90°, *F* = *BIl*   If *θ* = 30°, *F* = *BIl* × 0.5   If *θ* = 0°, *F* = 0

Use a *Digital Balance* to *Investigate* Flux Density

You can use the set-up shown to investigate the **uniform magnetic field** between the poles of a magnet and obtain a value for **flux density, *B***. You should use magnets with **poles** on their **largest** faces.

1) A **square hoop** of metal wire is positioned so that the **top** of the hoop, **length *l***, passes through the magnetic field, **perpendicular** to it. When a current flows, the **length of wire** in the magnetic field will experience a downwards **force** (Fleming's left hand rule).

2) The power supply should be connected to a **variable resistor** so that you can **alter** the **current**. Zero the digital balance when there is **no** current through the wire so that the mass reading is due to the electromagnetic force only. Then turn on the power supply.

3) Note the **mass** and the **current**. Use the variable resistor to **change** the current and record the new mass — do this for a **large range** of currents. Repeat this twice to give 3 mass readings for each current.

4) Calculate the **mean** for each mass reading, then convert your mass readings into **force** using *F* = *mg*. **Plot** the data on a graph of **force *F*** against **current *I***, and draw a line of best fit.

5) Because ***F* = *BIl***, the **gradient** of your graph is equal to *B* × *l*. Measure the gradient, then divide by length *l* to **get a value for *B***.

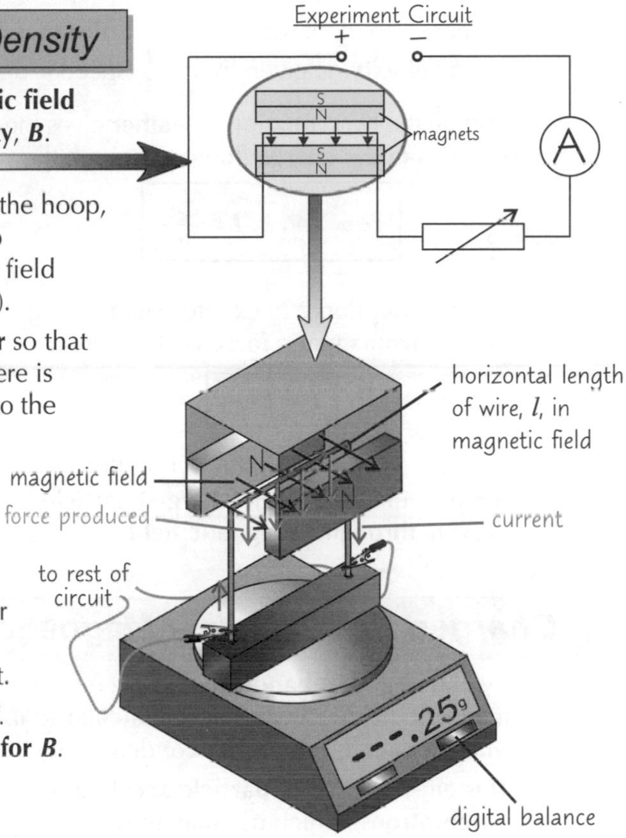

Experiment Circuit

magnets

horizontal length of wire, *l*, in magnetic field

magnetic field
force produced

current

to rest of circuit

digital balance

Practice Questions

Q1 What two things can cause a magnetic field?

Q2 Sketch the magnetic fields around a long straight current-carrying wire, a flat coil and a solenoid. Show the direction of the current and magnetic field on each diagram.

Q3 A copper bar can roll freely on two copper supports, as shown in the diagram. When current is applied in the direction shown, which way will the bar roll?

Q4 What is the definition of magnetic flux density? What are its units?

Q5 Describe an experiment you could carry out to determine the uniform magnetic flux density between the poles of a magnet.

magnets with poles on their largest faces

copper bar

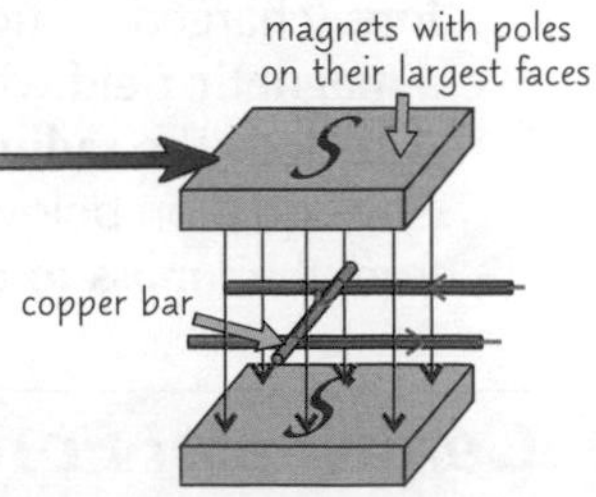

Exam Question

Q1 A 4.00 cm length of wire carrying a current of 3.00 A runs perpendicular to a magnetic field of strength 2.00×10^{-5} T.

a) Calculate the magnitude of the force on the wire.   [1 mark]

b) The wire is rotated so that it is at 30.0° to the direction of the field. Calculate the size of the force.   [1 mark]

I revised the right hand rule by the A69 and ended up in Newcastle...

Fleming's left hand rule is the key to this section — so make sure you know how to use it and understand what it all means. Remember that the direction of the magnetic field is from N to S, and that the current is from +ve to –ve — this is as important as using the correct hand. You need to get those right or it'll all go to pot...

Charged Particles in Magnetic Fields

Magnetic fields are used a lot when dealing with particle beams.

Forces Act on Charged Particles in Magnetic Fields

Electric current in a wire is caused by the **flow** of negatively **charged** electrons. These charged particles are affected by **magnetic fields** — so a current-carrying wire can experience a **force** in a magnetic field (see pages 50–51).

1) The equation for the **force** exerted on a **current-carrying wire** in a **magnetic field** perpendicular to the current is:

   | Equation 1: $F = BIl$ |

2) To see how this relates to **charged particles** moving through a wire, you need to know that electric **current**, I, is the flow of **charge**, Q, per unit **time**, t: $I = \dfrac{Q}{t}$

3) A charged particle which moves a **distance** l in **time** t has a **velocity**, v, given by $v = \dfrac{l}{t}$ (speed = dist ÷ time), so: $t = \dfrac{l}{v}$

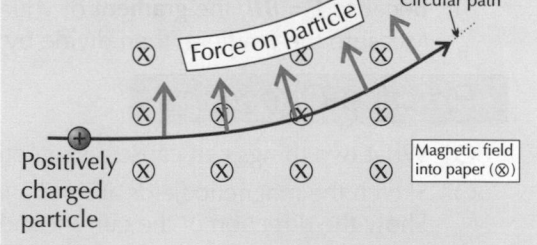

In many exam questions, Q is the size of the charge on the electron, which is 1.60×10^{-19} coulombs.

4) Putting the two equations **together** gives the **current** in terms of the **charge** flowing through the **wire**:

   | Equation 2: $I = \dfrac{Qv}{l}$ |

5) Putting **equation 2** back into **equation 1** gives the **electromagnetic force** on the wire as:

   | $F = BQv$ |

6) You can use this equation to find the **force** acting on a **single charged particle** moving through a magnetic field.

Example: An electron is travelling at 2.00×10^4 ms^{-1} perpendicular to the field lines of a uniform magnetic field of strength 2.00 T. Calculate the size of the force acting on the electron. (The magnitude of the charge on an electron is 1.60×10^{-19} C.)

$F = BQv$
so $F = 2.00 \times 1.60 \times 10^{-19} \times 2.00 \times 10^4$
$F = \mathbf{6.40 \times 10^{-15}}$ **N**

Charged Particles in a Magnetic Field are Deflected in a Circular Path

1) By **Fleming's left hand rule** the force on a **moving charge** in a magnetic field is always **perpendicular** to its **direction of travel**. Mathematically, that is the condition for **circular motion** (p.14).

2) This effect is used in **particle accelerators** such as **cyclotrons** and **synchrotrons**, which use **magnetic fields** to accelerate particles to very **high energies** along circular paths.

3) It's also used in **mass spectrometers** to analyse chemical samples. **Ions** (charged particles) with the **same velocity** are made to enter a **magnetic field** which deflects them in a curved path towards a detector. The **radius of curvature** depends on the **charge** and **mass** of the particles (see equation below). The **identity** of the ions reaching the detector can be deduced from their **mass to charge** ratio.

Circular path

Force on particle

Positively charged particle

| Magnetic field into paper (⊗) |

This is not a cyclotron.

Centripetal Force Tells Us About a Particle's Path

The centripetal force (see p.14) and the force due to the magnetic field are equivalent for a charged particle travelling along a circular path.

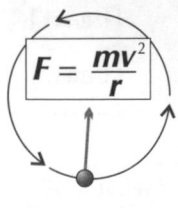

$F = \dfrac{mv^2}{r}$

Centripetal force

$F = BQv$

Electromagnetic force

1) For uniform circular motion **Newton's second law** gives: $F = \dfrac{mv^2}{r}$

2) So, for a **charged particle** following a **circular** path in a **magnetic field** (where $F = BQv$): $BQv = \dfrac{mv^2}{r}$

3) Rearranging gives:

   | $r = \dfrac{mv}{BQ}$ | Where: m is the mass of the particle, v is its speed and r is the radius of the circular path.

Charged Particles in Magnetic Fields

Velocity Selectors Use Both Magnetic and Electric Fields

Velocity selectors are used to **separate** out particles of a **certain velocity** from a stream of **accelerated charged particles** moving at a **range of speeds**. They do this by applying **both** a magnetic and an electric field at the **same time** perpendicular to each other, while a stream of particles is fired perpendicularly to both fields at a device with a narrow gap called a **collimator**.

> For the examples on this page:
> The electric field, E, goes **top** to **bottom** (i.e. down the page). The magnetic field, B, goes straight into the page.

1) Particles fired into the velocity selector experience **opposing forces** from the electric and magnetic fields:

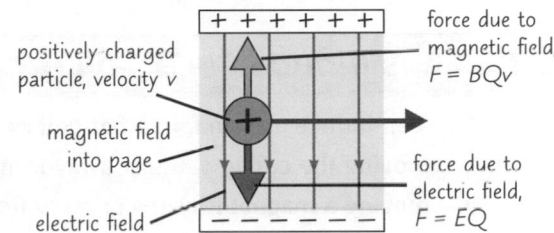

- The **magnetic** field tries to deflect particles **upwards** — check this with Fleming's left hand rule. The force on each particle is $F = BQv$ (see previous page).
- The **electric** field tries to deflect particles **downwards** (opposite charges attract, like charges repel). The force on the particle is $F = EQ$ (see p.46).

2) Particles will be **deflected** unless the forces balance (i.e. $BQv = EQ$). Cancelling Qs and rearranging gives:

$$v = \frac{E}{B}$$

3) So **only** particles with **velocity** $v = \frac{E}{B}$ as given above will travel in a **straight line** to pass through the gap in the **collimator**.

4) You can select and vary the **velocity** of the particles that get through the collimator by **changing** the **strength** of the magnetic or electric fields.

5) Velocity selectors are often used in **mass spectrometers** to ensure that the accelerated particles entering the magnetic field have the same velocity.

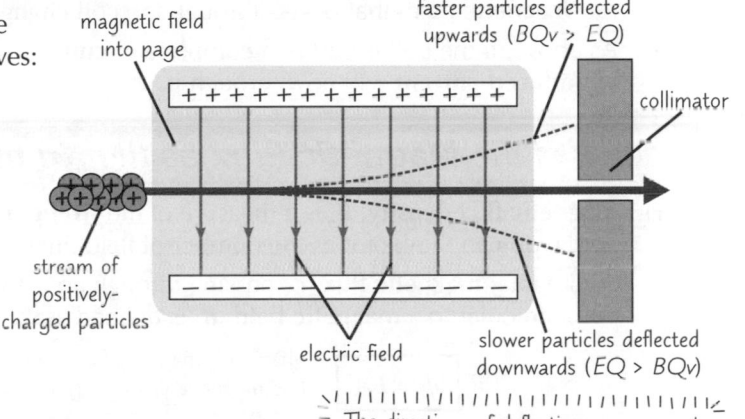

> The directions of deflection are reversed for negatively-charged particles.

Practice Questions

Q1 Derive the formula for the force on a charged particle in a magnetic field, $F = BQv$, from $F = BIl$.

Q2 Briefly describe two applications of charged particles being deflected in a circular field in a magnetic field.

Q3 Describe how a velocity selector works, including the roles of the electric and magnetic fields.

Exam Questions

Elementary charge = 1.60×10^{-19} C, electron rest mass = 9.11×10^{-31} kg,

Q1 a) An electron is travelling at a velocity of 5.00×10^6 ms^{-1} through a perpendicular magnetic field of 0.770 T. Calculate the magnitude of the force acting on the electron. [2 marks]

b) Explain why the electron follows a circular path while in the field. [1 mark]

Q2 Calculate the radius of the circular path of an electron with a velocity of 2.30×10^7 ms^{-1} moving perpendicular to a magnetic field of 0.600 mT. [3 marks]

Q3 A sample of sodium chloride is analysed using a mass spectrometer. The magnetic field is initially set to 0.200 T and ions of the isotope Cl-35 (mass 35 u) reach the same point on the detector. Calculate the magnetic field strength you would need for Cl-37 ions (mass 37 u) to reach the same point on the detector. Assume that both types of ion have the same charge as an electron and that all ions enter the magnetic field with the same velocity. [3 marks]

Hold on to your hats folks — this is starting to get tricky...

Basically, the main thing you need to know here is that both electric and magnetic fields will exert a force on a charged particle. There's even a handy equation to work out the force on a charged particle moving through a magnetic field.

Electromagnetic Induction

Producing electricity by waggling a wire about in a magnetic field sounds like magic — but it's real physics...

E.m.f. is Induced in a Conducting Rod Moving Through a Magnetic Field

1) If there is relative motion between a **conducting rod** and a magnetic field, the **electrons in the rod** will experience a **force** (see p.50), which causes them to **accumulate** at one end of the rod.

2) This **induces** an **electromotive force** (**e.m.f.**) across the ends of the rod exactly as connecting a battery to it would — this is called **electromagnetic induction**.

3) If the rod is part of a complete **circuit**, then an induced current will **flow** through it.

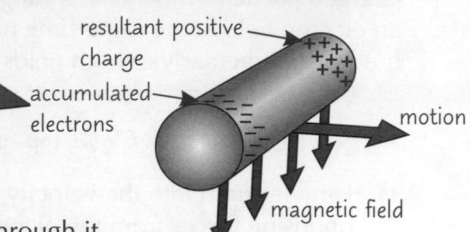

E.m.f. is Induced in a Coil experiencing a Changing Magnetic Field

1) You can induce an e.m.f. in a **flat coil** or **solenoid** by:
   • **moving the coil** towards or away from the poles of a magnet.
   • **moving a magnet** towards or away from the coil.

2) In either case, the e.m.f. is a caused by the **magnetic field** (or '**magnetic flux**') that passes through the coil **changing**.

3) As above, if the coil is part of a **complete circuit**, an **induced current** will flow through it.

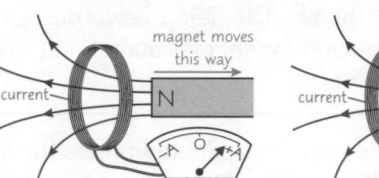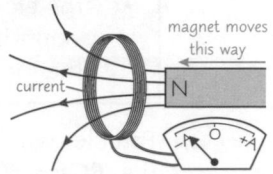

Think of the Magnetic Flux as the Number of Field Lines

1) **Magnetic flux density, B**, is a measure of the **strength** of the magnetic field (you can think of it as the number of field lines per unit area).

2) So the total **magnetic flux**, ϕ, passing through an **area, A**, perpendicular to a **magnetic field, B**, is defined as:

$$\phi = BA$$

where ϕ is magnetic flux in webers (Wb), B is magnetic flux density (T) and A is area (m^2).

3) You can think of **flux** as the **number of field lines**. But remember that flux is **continuous** — field lines are just a way of **drawing it**.

4) The diagram to the right shows magnetic flux inside a **single loop coil**. The flux inside the coil is $\phi = BA$, where A = area of coil.

5) If you have a **coil of N turns**, rather than a single loop, you need to talk about **flux linkage** instead which is just flux multiplied by N:

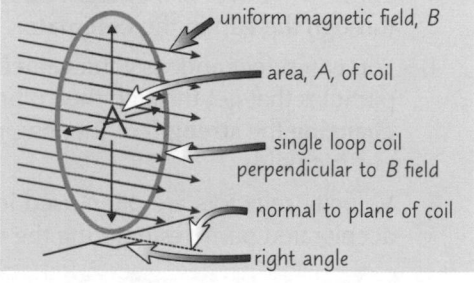

flux linkage = $N\phi$ units of flux linkage are also Wb

Use Trig if the Magnetic Flux Isn't Perpendicular to the Area

1) When the magnetic flux **isn't perpendicular** to the area of the coil you're interested in, you need to use **trigonometry** to find the component of the flux that is **perpendicular** to the area.

2) If θ is the **angle** between the **magnetic flux** and the **normal to the plane** of the coil, you get:

$$\phi = BA\cos\theta$$ for a single loop coil

$$\text{flux linkage} = N\phi = BAN\cos\theta$$ for a coil of N turns

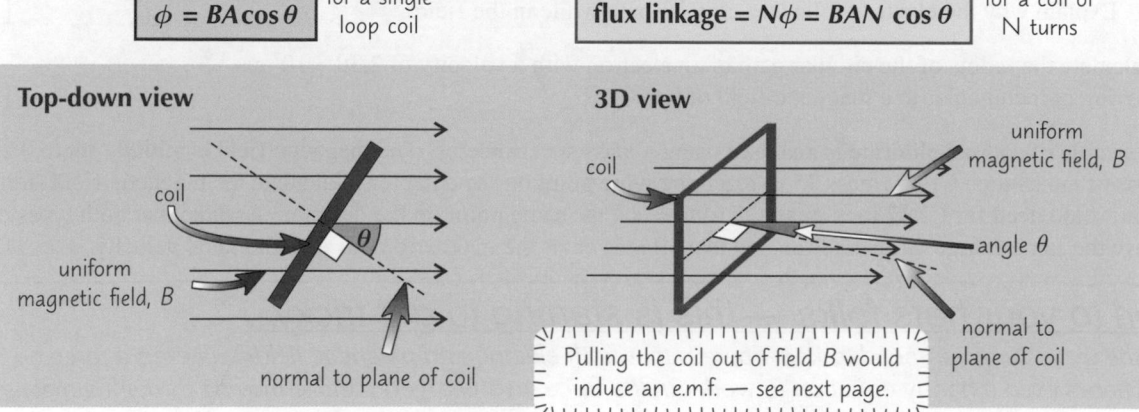

Electromagnetic Induction

These Results are Summed up by Faraday's Law...

> **FARADAY'S LAW:** The **induced e.m.f.** is **directly proportional** to the **rate of change of flux linkage**.

It can be written as:

$$\text{Induced e.m.f., } \varepsilon = -\frac{\text{flux linkage change}}{\text{time taken}} = -\frac{\Delta(N\phi)}{\Delta t} = -\frac{N\Delta\phi}{\Delta t}$$

> The minus sign is Lenz's law — see next page.
> $N = 1$ if it's just a single loop or rod.

1) The formula above can be applied to a **coil** or **conducting rod**.

2) For a coil, induced e.m.f. depends on the number of turns and **how fast** flux through the coil is changing.

3) For a conducting rod, think of flux change as field lines being 'cut' as the rod moves (see next page).

4) The unit of flux, the **weber** (**Wb**), is defined in terms of the e.m.f. induced:

> A **change** in **flux linkage** of **one weber per second** will induce an **electromotive force** of **1 volt** in a loop of wire.

Faraday's Law on Graphs:

1) The **size** of the **e.m.f.** is shown by the **gradient** of a graph of flux linkage against time.

2) The **area under** the graph of e.m.f. against time gives the **flux linkage change**.

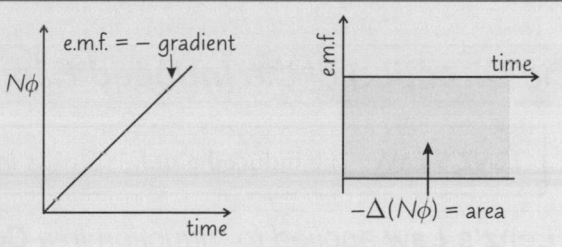

Practice Questions

Q1 What is the difference between magnetic flux density, magnetic flux and magnetic flux linkage?

Q2 Give the equations for flux linkage in an N-turn coil at right angles and at angle θ to a magnetic field.

Q3 State Faraday's law and give the definition of the weber.

Q4 What does the gradient of a graph of flux linkage against time tell you?

Q5 How can you find the change in flux linkage from a graph of e.m.f. against time?

Exam Questions

Q1 The magnetic flux density of a uniform magnetic field is 2.00×10^{-3} T.

  a) Calculate the magnetic flux passing through an area of 0.230 m^2 at right angles to the field lines. [1 mark]

  b) A coil of area 0.230 m^2 with 151 turns is placed in the field at right angles to the field lines. Calculate the magnetic flux linkage in the coil. [1 mark]

  c) Over a period of 2.50 seconds the magnetic field is reduced uniformly to 1.50×10^{-3} T. Calculate the e.m.f. induced across the ends of the coil. [3 marks]

Q2 A 0.010 m^2 coil of 550 turns is perpendicular to a magnetic field of strength 0.92 T generated.

  a) Calculate the magnetic flux linkage in the coil. [1 mark]

  b) The coil is rotated until the normal to the plane of the coil is at $90°$ to the magnetic field. The movement is uniform and takes 0.5 s. Calculate the e.m.f. induced by this movement. [2 marks]

Q3 The graph shows how the flux linkage through a coil varies over time. Sketch a graph to show how the induced e.m.f. in the coil varies over this same time period.

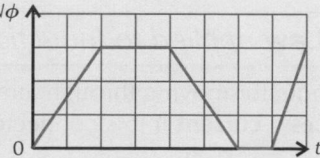

[3 marks]

Beware — physics can induce extreme confusion...

Make sure you know the difference between flux and flux linkage, and that you can calculate both even when they aren't perpendicular to area and you have to get some pesky trigonometry involved. This is a tricky topic so if I were you, I'd head back to the start and go through it all again even more carefully — don't let it catch you out in the exams.

Electromagnetic Induction

A bit more on Faraday's Law, then we move on to his partner in crime, Lenz...

Faraday's Law Gives E.m.f. of a **Conducting Rod** in terms of **Velocity**

1) For a rod moving across a **magnetic field**, e.m.f. is induced as the rod '**cuts**' magnetic flux (field lines).

2) Remember that magnetic flux $\phi = BA$ (see p.54) — here, think of A as the **area of flux cut** in a certain time.

3) Faraday's equation can be **used** to find the **e.m.f.** in terms of the rod's speed:

Example: A conducting rod of length l moves through a perpendicular uniform magnetic field, B, at a constant velocity, v. Show that the e.m.f. induced in the rod is equal to $-Blv$.

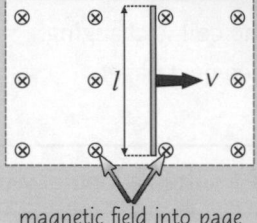

magnetic field into page

Distance travelled, $s = v\Delta t$ (distance = speed × time)

Area of flux it cuts, $A = lv\Delta t$

Total magnetic flux cut through, $\Delta\phi = BA = Blv\Delta t$

Faraday's law gives $\varepsilon = -\dfrac{\Delta(N\phi)}{\Delta t} = -\dfrac{\Delta\phi}{\Delta t}$ (since $N = 1$)

So induced e.m.f., $\varepsilon = -\dfrac{\Delta\phi}{\Delta t} = -\dfrac{Blv\Delta t}{\Delta t} = -Blv$

You might be asked to find the e.m.f. induced on something more interesting than a rod, e.g. the Earth's magnetic field across the wingspan of a plane. Just think of it as a moving rod and use the equation as usual.

The **Direction** of the **Induced E.m.f.** and **Current** are given by **Lenz's Law**

LENZ'S LAW: The **induced e.m.f.** is always in such a **direction** as to **oppose** the **change** that caused it.

This is why there's a **minus sign** in Faraday's Law.

Lenz's Law applied to Induction in a **Coil**

1) A changing magnetic field **induces an e.m.f.** in a coil (see previous page).

2) If the coil is part of a **complete** circuit, a **current** is induced in the **same direction** as the induced **e.m.f.**

3) The **induced current** then produces its own **magnetic field** (p.50). Lenz's law says:

- If the **original** magnetic field is getting **stronger**, the **induced** magnetic field will be in the **opposite direction** to try to **weaken** it.

- If the **original** magnetic field is getting **weaker** (collapsing), the **induced** magnetic field will be in the **same direction** to try to **maintain** it.

Kevin's lenses always acted in the opposite direction.

Example: The area of a flat coil is perpendicular to a magnetic field as it collapses by 50% as shown below. What will be the direction of the current induced in the loop?

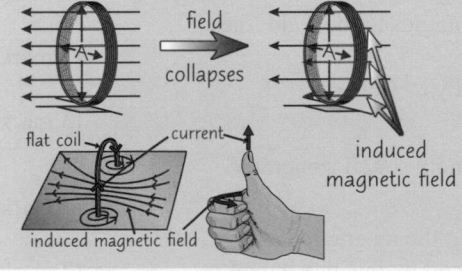

A **collapsing** field means the field is getting **weaker** and the field lines are getting **further apart** (p.50). So by Lenz's law the current induced in the coil will **induce a magnetic field** in the **same direction** as the **collapsing** field to try to **maintain** the **original** field.

Use the **right-hand rule** (p.50) to find the direction of the induced current. The induced **field** is to the **left**, so the induced **current** is **clockwise** when viewed from the right.

Lenz's Law applied to Induction in a **Conducting Rod**

- A conductor moving through a magnetic field **induces a current** if it is connected to a circuit.

- **Lenz's law** says that the **induced current** will produce a **force to oppose** the motion of the conductor (a **resistance**).

- You know the directions of the **magnetic field** and the induced **resistance force**, so you can use **Fleming's left hand rule** (see p.50) to find the direction of the **induced current** and so the direction of the induced **e.m.f.**

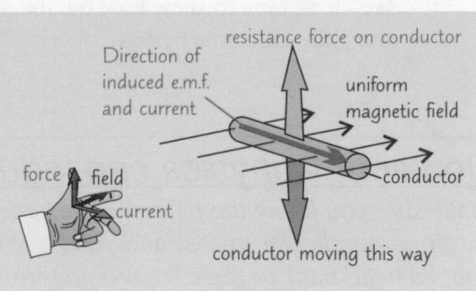

Electromagnetic Induction

You can use Faraday's Law and Lenz's Law to Investigate Magnetic Flux

This set up shows how you can find the magnetic flux density, B, using a search coil and a data logger...

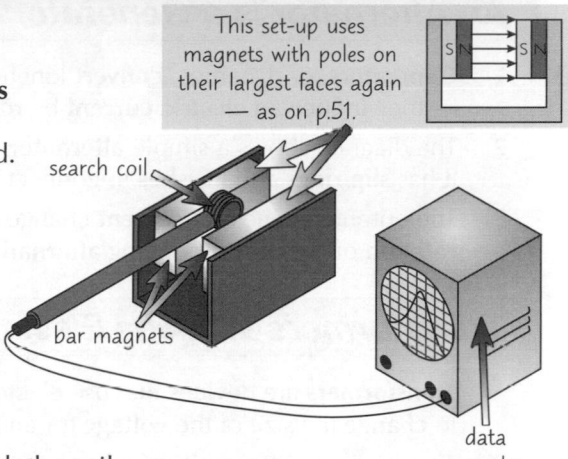

This set-up uses magnets with poles on their largest faces again — as on p.51.

1) Place two **bar magnets** a small distance apart with **opposite poles facing** each other — they should be far enough apart not to snap together, but otherwise as close as possible to give a uniform field.

2) Get a **search coil** — this is a small coil of wire with a **known number of turns** (N) and a **known area** (A). Connect it to a **data recorder** and set the recorder to measure the **induced e.m.f.** with a **very small time interval** between readings.

3) Place the search coil in the **middle** of the magnetic field so that the area (A) of the coil is parallel to the surface of the magnets. Start the data recorder. Keeping the coil in the **same orientation**, immediately move the coil out of the field.

4) An e.m.f. will be induced due to the magnetic flux density through the coil changing from **maximum** to **zero** as you **remove** the coil from the **field**.

5) Use your data or the data recorder to plot a graph of **induced e.m.f.** against **time**.

6) Using Faraday's and Lenz's Laws, estimating the **area under the graph** of e.m.f. against time gives you an estimate for the **total flux linkage change** (p.55).

7) **Flux linkage = $N\phi = BAN$** (p.54), so to **find B**, divide the total flux linkage change by coil area (A) and number of turns (N).

8) **Repeat** this experiment several times and find the mean of your values for B.

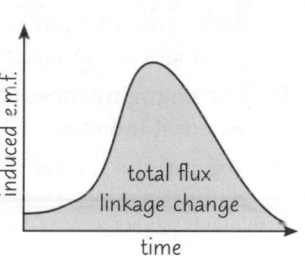

Practice Questions

Q1 State Lenz's law.

Q2 Describe how to determine the direction of the induced current when:
   a) a coil moves perpendicularly through the field lines of a magnetic field, with the area of the coil perpendicular to the field lines.
   b) a conducting rod moves through a magnetic field with the length of the rod perpendicular to the field lines.

Q3 Describe an experiment you could carry out to investigate magnetic flux using a search coil.

Exam Questions

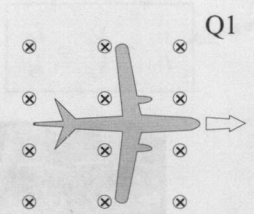

Q1 An aeroplane with a wingspan of 33.9 m flies at a speed of 148 ms⁻¹ perpendicular to the Earth's magnetic field, as shown. The Earth's magnetic field at the aeroplane's location is 6.00×10^{-5} T. The magnetic field in the diagram goes into the page.

   a) Calculate the induced e.m.f. between the wing tips. [3 marks]

   b) Copy and complete the diagram to show the direction of the induced e.m.f. between the wing-tips. [1 mark]

Q2 A flat coil of 75 turns with an area of 0.030 m² is placed in a uniform magnetic field generated by an electromagnet. The area of the coil is perpendicular to the field lines.

   a) The electromagnet is initially turned off. The power supply is switched on and the current is increased so that the magnetic field strength linearly increases from 0 to 150 mT in 7.5 seconds. Calculate size of the e.m.f. induced in the coil. [2 marks]

   b) The coil is part of a complete circuit. State the direction the induced current will flow through the coil and explain why this is the case. [2 marks]

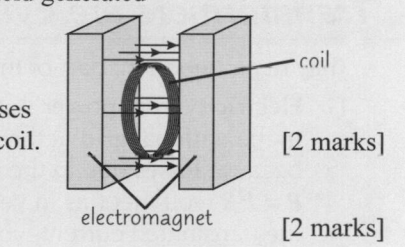

Don't steal camera Lenzs — the law will catch you before you get Far away...

Far away... Far aday... Faraday... geddit? No? I really don't know why I bother sometimes. Anyway, don't worry if this stuff doesn't make complete (or any) sense at first... Lenz's law is particularly horrible. Just keep going over the page until slowly but surely the penny begins to drop. Then pick up the penny and err... add it to your coin collection.

Uses of Electromagnetic Induction

Faraday's law of electromagnetic induction turns up all over the place — from phone chargers to power stations...

An **Alternator** is a **Generator** of **Alternating Current**

1) **Generators**, or dynamos, **convert** kinetic energy into **electrical energy** — they **induce** an electric **current** by **rotating** a **coil** in a magnetic field.

2) The diagram shows a simple **alternator** — a generator of **a.c.** It has **slip rings** and **brushes** to connect the coil to an external circuit.

3) The output **voltage** and **current** change direction with every **half rotation** of the coil, producing **alternating current** (a.c.).

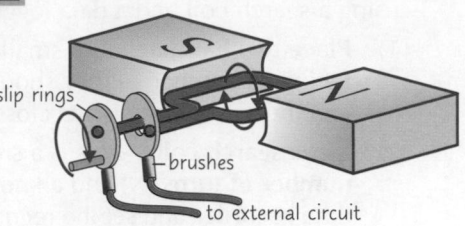
slip rings
brushes
to external circuit

Transformers Work by Electromagnetic **Induction**

1) **Transformers** are devices that use electromagnetic induction to **change** the size of the **voltage** for an **alternating current**.

2) They consist of **two coils of wire** wrapped around an **iron core**.

3) An alternating current flowing in the **primary** (or input) **coil** produces a changing **magnetic field** in the **iron core**.

laminated iron core
magnetic field in the iron core
primary coil
secondary coil

4) The **changing magnetic field** is passed through the **iron core** to the **secondary** (or output) coil, where it **induces** an alternating **voltage** (e.m.f.) of the same frequency as the input voltage.

5) The **ratio** of the **number of turns** on each coil along with the voltage across the primary coil determines the **size of the voltage** induced in the secondary coil.

> **Step-up** transformers **increase** the **voltage** by having **more turns** on the **secondary** coil than the primary.
> **Step-down** transformers **reduce** the voltage by having **fewer** turns on the secondary coil.

6) Real-life transformers **aren't 100% efficient** — some power is always lost. Using a **laminated core** reduces losses.

You Can **Calculate** the **Induced E.m.f.s** in **Each Coil**

From Faraday's law (page 55), the **induced** e.m.f.s in both the **primary** (*p*) and **secondary** (*s*) coils can be calculated:

Primary coil
$$V_p = -\frac{n_p \Delta\phi}{\Delta t}$$

Secondary coil
$$V_s = -\frac{n_s \Delta\phi}{\Delta t}$$

(where *n* is the number of turns in a coil)

Ideal transformers are **100% efficient**, so **power in** equals the **power out**.

Power is **current × voltage**, so for an ideal transformer $I_p V_p = I_s V_s$, or $\frac{I_p}{I_s} = \frac{V_s}{V_p}$.

Combine this with the equations for induced e.m.f. in each coil to get the **transformer equation**...

$$\frac{n_s}{n_p} = \frac{V_s}{V_p} = \frac{I_p}{I_s}$$

> **Example:** What is the output voltage for a transformer with a primary coil of 120 turns, a secondary coil of 350 turns and an input voltage of 230 V?
>
> $$\frac{n_s}{n_p} = \frac{V_s}{V_p} \qquad V_s = \frac{V_p \times n_s}{n_p} = \frac{230 \times 350}{120} = 670.83... = \mathbf{670\ V}\ \textbf{(to 2 s.f.)}$$

... robots in disguise

Transformers are Everywhere

They're an important part of the national grid...

1) **Electricity** from power stations is sent round the country in the **national grid** at the **lowest** possible current. This is because **losses** due to the **resistance** in the cables is equal to $P = I^2 R$ (you met this in year 1 of A-level) — so if you double the transmitted current, you **quadruple** the power lost.

2) Since **power = current × voltage**, a **low current** means a **high voltage**.

3) **Transformers** allow us to **step up** the voltage to around **400 000 V** for **transmission** through the national grid, and then **reduce** it again in substations to **230 V** for home use.

...and are in loads of your devices.

1) Lots of **electronic devices** like laptops, mobiles, monitors and speakers **can't function** using a standard **230 V** mains supply — they need a **much lower voltage** (and usually a d.c. supply too).

2) The **chargers** for these devices contain **transformers** to adjust the voltage — they're contained in the **plug** or a **box** in the cable.

Uses of Electromagnetic Induction

Investigate the **Number of Turns**, **Voltage** and **Current** in a Transformer

To investigate the relationship between **number of turns** and the **voltages** across the coils:

1) Set up the equipment as shown. Put two C-cores together and wrap wire around each to make the coils. Begin with 5 turns in the primary coil and 10 in the secondary coil (a **ratio** of 1:2).

2) Turn on the a.c. supply to the primary coil. **Use a low voltage** — remember transformers **increase voltage**, so make sure you keep it at a safe level. Record the voltage across each coil.

3) Keeping V_p the same so it's a fair test, repeat the experiment with different ratios of turns. Try 1:1 and 2:1. Divide n_s by n_p and V_s by V_p. You should find that for each ratio of turns, $\frac{n_s}{n_p} = \frac{V_s}{V_p}$.

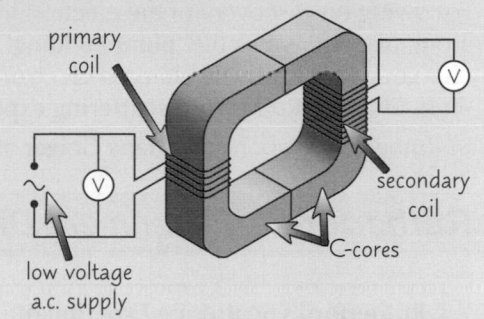

primary coil

secondary coil

C-cores

low voltage a.c. supply

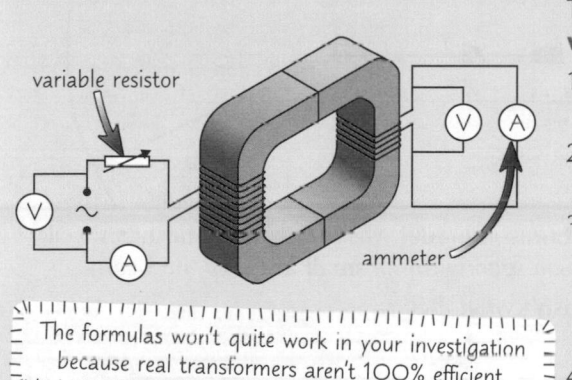

variable resistor

ammeter

~\|\|\|\|\|\|\|\|\|\|\|\|\|\|\|\|\|\|\|\|\|\|\|\|\|\|\|\|\|\|\|\|\|\|\|\|\|\|\|\|\|\|\|\|\|\|~
The formulas won't quite work in your investigation because real transformers aren't 100% efficient.
~\|\|\|\|\|\|\|\|\|\|\|\|\|\|\|\|\|\|\|\|\|\|\|\|\|\|\|\|\|\|\|\|\|\|\|\|\|\|\|\|\|~

To investigate the relationship between **number of turns**, **voltage** across and **current** of the transformer coils:

1) Use the same equipment as above, but add a **variable resistor** to the primary coil circuit and an **ammeter** to both circuits.

2) Turn on the power supply and **record the current through** and **voltage across** each coil.

3) Leaving the number of turns **constant**, adjust the variable resistor to change the input current. Record the current and voltage for each coil, then **repeat** this process for a **range** of input currents.

4) You should find that for each current, $\frac{n_s}{n_p} = \frac{V_s}{V_p} = \frac{I_p}{I_s}$.

Practice Questions

Q1 Sketch and label a diagram of an a.c. generator. How does it work?

Q2 Draw a diagram of a simple transformer. What is meant by a step-down transformer?

Q3 Describe the role of transformers in the national grid.

Q4 Describe an experiment to investigate how the ratio of number of turns in the primary and secondary coils of a transformer affects the current and voltage in the secondary coil.

Exam Questions

Q1 A transformer with 158 turns in the primary coil has an input voltage of 9.30 V.

   a) i) Calculate the number of turns needed in the secondary coil to step up the voltage to 45.0 V.   [1 mark]

      ii) The secondary coil actually has 90.0 turns. Calculate the voltage induced in the secondary coil.   [1 mark]

   b) The input current for the transformer is 1.50 A.
      Assuming the transformer is ideal, calculate the output current.   [1 mark]

Q2 A substation receives 943 kW of electricity from a power station through wires with a total resistance 132 Ω.
The input current was 15.6 A.

   a) Calculate the electrical power originally transmitted from the power station.   [2 marks]

   b) Describe how transformers are used in the transmission of electricity at a low current, explaining why this is important.   [2 marks]

Aaaaaand — relax...

Breathe a sigh of relief, pat yourself on the back and make a brew — well done, you've reached the end of the section. That was pretty nasty stuff (the section, not your tea), but don't let all of those equations get you down — once you've learnt the main ones and can use them blindfolded, even the trickiest looking exam question will be a walk in the park.

Atomic Structure

We have a pretty good idea of atomic structure these days — but it's been anything but plain sailing...

The **Thomson Model** said **Electrons** were **Spread Out** Inside an **Atom**

Following his discovery of the electron in the late 19th century, **J.J. Thomson** proposed the **Thomson model** of the atom, also known as the '**plum pudding**' model. This model said that atoms were made up of a globule of **positive charge**, with **negatively charged electrons sprinkled** in it, like fruit in a plum pudding. It was widely accepted at the time, until the **Rutherford scattering experiment** of 1909.

In Rutherford's laboratory, **Hans Geiger** and **Ernest Marsden** studied the scattering of **alpha particles** by **thin metal foils**.

Rutherford's Experiment **Disproved** the **Thomson Model**...

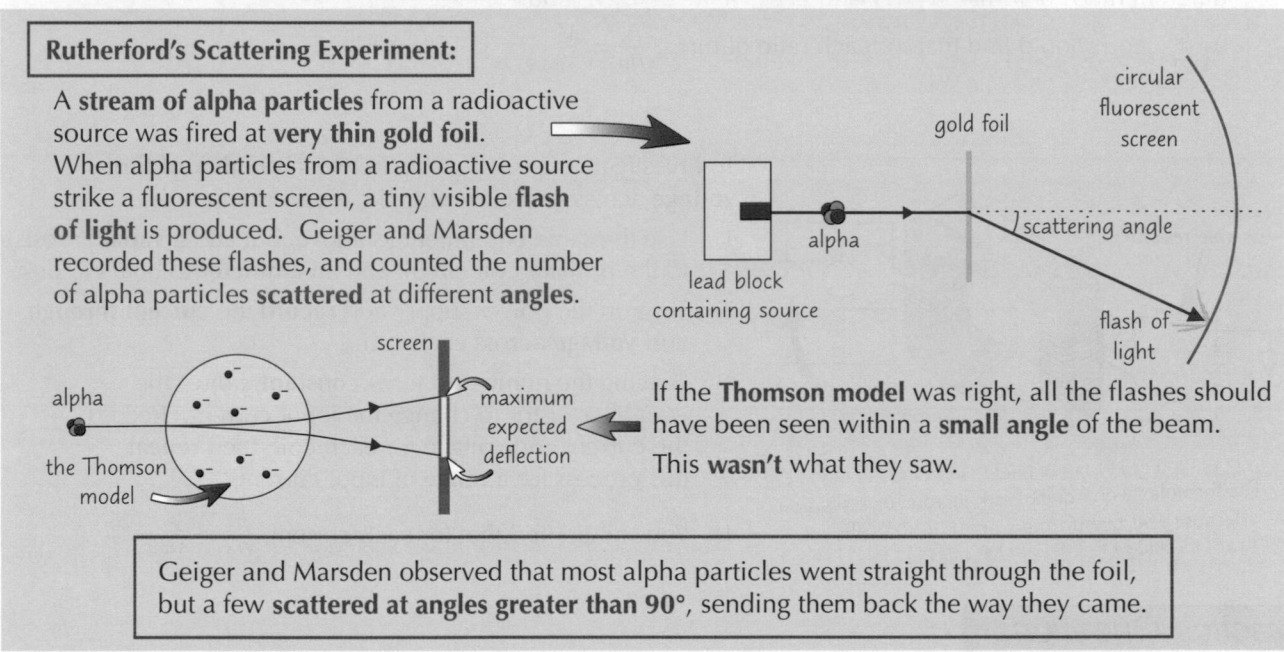

Rutherford's Scattering Experiment:

A **stream of alpha particles** from a radioactive source was fired at **very thin gold foil**. When alpha particles from a radioactive source strike a fluorescent screen, a tiny visible **flash of light** is produced. Geiger and Marsden recorded these flashes, and counted the number of alpha particles **scattered** at different **angles**.

If the **Thomson model** was right, all the flashes should have been seen within a **small angle** of the beam. This **wasn't** what they saw.

Geiger and Marsden observed that most alpha particles went straight through the foil, but a few **scattered at angles greater than 90°**, sending them back the way they came.

...and Supported the Idea of a **Small**, **Positively Charged Nucleus**

This experiment led Rutherford to some **important conclusions**:

1) Most of the fast, charged alpha particles went **straight through** the foil. So the atom is mainly **empty space**.

2) **Some** of the alpha particles were **deflected** through **large angles**, so the **centre** of the atom must have a **large**, **positive charge** to repel them. Rutherford named this the **nucleus**.

3) Very few particles were deflected by angles greater than **90 degrees**, so the nucleus must be **tiny**.

4) Most of the **mass** must be in the nucleus, since the fast alpha particles (with high momentum) are deflected by the nucleus.

So most of the **mass** and the **positive charge** in an atom must be contained within a **tiny**, **central nucleus**.

The **Nuclear Model** Explained **Rutherford Scattering**

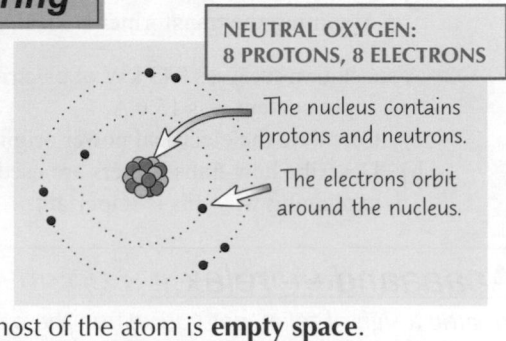

NEUTRAL OXYGEN: 8 PROTONS, 8 ELECTRONS

The nucleus contains protons and neutrons.

The electrons orbit around the nucleus.

1) Inside **every atom**, there's a **positive nucleus** containing **neutrons** (which have no charge) and **positively charged protons**. Protons and **neutrons** are both known as **nucleons**. **Orbiting** this core are the **negatively charged electrons**.

2) The **charge** on an **electron**, $-e$, is **equal and opposite** to the charge on a **proton**, $+e$. e is the **elementary charge** 1.60×10^{-19} C.

3) The **nucleus** only makes up a tiny proportion of an atom — it's only about **one 10 000th of the size** of the whole atom. The electrons orbit at relatively **vast distances** from the nucleus, so most of the atom is **empty space**.

4) The **proton** and **neutron** are roughly **2000 times** more **massive** than the **electron**, so the nucleus makes up **nearly all** of the **mass** of the atom.

Atomic Structure

The Proton Number is the Number of Protons in the Nucleus

No... really.

The **proton number** is sometimes called the **atomic number**, and has the **symbol Z** (don't ask me why).
Z is just the **number of protons** in the nucleus.

It's the **proton number** that **defines** the **element** — **no two elements** will have the **same** number of protons.

In a **neutral atom**, the number of **electrons equals** the number of **protons**. The element's **reactions** and **chemical behaviour** depend on the number of **electrons**. So the **proton number** tells you a lot about its **chemical properties**.

The Nucleon Number is the Total Number of Protons and Neutrons

The **nucleon number** is also called the **mass number**, and has the **symbol A** (*shrug*).
It tells you how many **protons** and **neutrons** are in the nucleus.

Each **proton or neutron** has a **mass** of (approximately) **1 atomic mass unit** (1.661×10^{-27} kg, see p.76).
The mass of an electron compared with a nucleon is virtually nothing, so the **number** of **nucleons** is about the same as the **atom's mass** (in atomic mass units).

Nuclei can be Represented Using Standard Notation

Standard notation summarises the important information about an element's **atomic structure**:

The **proton number** or **atomic number** (Z) — there are six protons in a carbon atom.

$$^{12}_{6}C$$

The **nucleon number** or **mass number** (A) — there are a total of 12 protons and neutrons in a carbon-12 atom.

The symbol for the element carbon.

Isotopes have the Same Proton Number, but Different Nucleon Numbers

Atoms with the **same number of protons** but **different numbers of neutrons** are called **isotopes**.

1) **Changing** the number of **neutrons doesn't affect** the atom's **chemical** properties.

2) The **number of neutrons** affects the **stability** of the nucleus though (see p.70).

3) **Unstable nuclei** may be **radioactive**.

4) Isotopes are often named using their **nucleon number**, e.g. carbon's isotopes include carbon-12 and carbon-13. Other isotopes have **special names** e.g. deuterium and tritium.

Example: Hydrogen has three naturally occurring isotopes: hydrogen, deuterium and tritium.

Hydrogen has **1 proton** and **0 neutrons**.
Deuterium has **1 proton** and **1 neutron**.
Tritium has **1 proton** and **2 neutrons**.

Practice Questions

Q1 List the particles that make up the atom and give their charges and relative masses.

Q2 Define the proton number and nucleon number.

Q3 What is an isotope?

Exam Questions

Q1 In 1911, Ernest Rutherford proposed the nuclear model of the atom after experiments using alpha-particle scattering.

a) Describe the nuclear model of the atom. [3 marks]

b) Explain how the alpha-particle scattering experiment provided evidence for Rutherford's model. [3 marks]

Q2 State how many protons, neutrons and electrons there are in a (neutral) $^{139}_{57}La$ atom. [2 marks]

Alpha scattering — it's positively repulsive...

The important things to learn from these two pages are the nuclear model for the structure of the atom (i.e. a large mass nucleus surrounded by orbiting electrons) and how the alpha particle scattering experiment provides evidence that supports this model. Once you know that, take a deep breath — it's about to get a little more confusing.

The Nucleus

The tiny nucleus — such a weird place, but one that you need to become ultra familiar with. Lucky you.
There's a nice graph coming up on page 64 though, so at least there's something to look forward to...

The **Nucleus** is a **Very Small Part** of a Whole **Atom**

1) By **probing atoms** using scattering and diffraction methods, we know that the **diameter of an atom** is about 0.1 nm (1×10^{-10} m) and the diameter of the smallest **nucleus** is a few fm (1 fm = 1×10^{-15} m — pronounced "femtometres").

2) So basically, **nuclei** are really, really **tiny** compared with the size of the **whole atom**.

3) To make this **easier to visualise**, try imagining a **large Ferris wheel** (which is pretty darn big) as the size of **an atom**. If you then put a **grain of rice** (which is rather small) in the centre, this would be the size of the atom's **nucleus**.

4) **Molecules** are just a number of **atoms joined together**. As a rough guide, the size of a molecule equals the number of atoms in it multiplied by the size of one atom.

I've seen bigger...

Nuclear Radius is Proportional to the Cube Root of the Nucleon Number

1) As you know from p.61, the **particles** that make up the nucleus (i.e. **protons** and **neutrons**) are called **nucleons**. The **number of nucleons** in an atom is called the **nucleon** (or **mass**) **number, A**.

2) Unsurprisingly, as **more nucleons** are added to the nucleus, it gets **bigger**.

3) You can measure the size of a nucleus by firing particles at it. If you plot the **radius of the nucleus**, **R**, against the **nucleon number**, you get a graph like this:

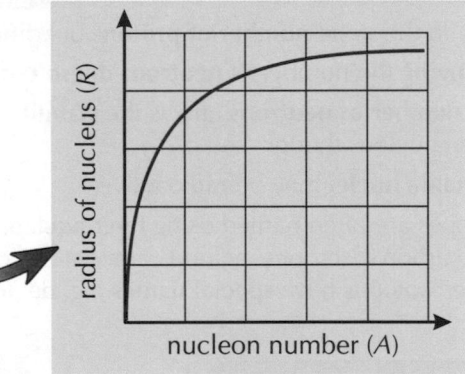

4) In fact, **nuclear radius** increases roughly as the **cube root** of the **nucleon number**. You can see this by plotting **nuclear radius** against the cube root of the **nucleon number**.

5) The fact that this graph is a **straight** line through the origin shows that nuclear radius is **directly proportional** to the cube root of the nucleon number. This relationship can be written as: $R \propto A^{1/3}$.

6) By introducing a constant, r_0, we can make this into an equation:

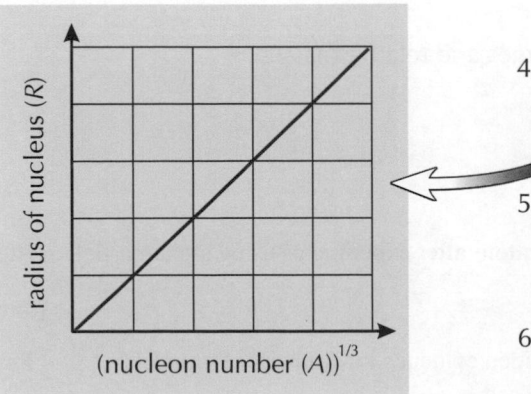

$$R = r_0 A^{1/3}$$

Where r_0 is about 1.4 fm or 1.4×10^{-15} m.

The Nucleus

Nuclear Density is Much Higher than Atomic Density

1) To calculate the **mean density** of a **nucleus** you need to know the **mass** and **volume** of the nucleus — and the equation for density:

$$\rho = \frac{m}{V}$$

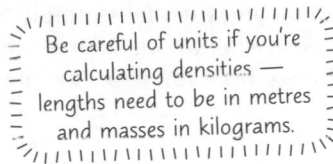
The symbol for density, ρ, is the Greek letter 'rho'. Its unit is $kg\,m^{-3}$.

2) If you're asked to **estimate mean nuclear density**, you might have to **work out** the **volume** of the nucleus from its **radius**. So, just assume the nucleus is a **sphere** and bung the value into the equation:

$$V = \frac{4}{3}\pi r^3$$

3) Nuclear density is **pretty much the same**, regardless of the element — roughly 10^{17} $kg\,m^{-3}$.

4) Nuclear density is **much higher** than atomic density. This suggests that:

- Most of an atom's mass is in its **nucleus**.
- The nucleus is **small** compared to the atom.
- An atom must contain a lot of **empty space**.

Be careful of units if you're calculating densities — lengths need to be in metres and masses in kilograms.

Example: A carbon atom has a mass of 2.00×10^{-26} kg, an atomic radius of 7.0×10^{-11} m, and a nuclear radius of 3.2×10^{-15} m.
a) Calculate its mean atomic density.   b) Calculate its mean nuclear density.

a) $V_{atom} = \frac{4}{3}\pi r^3 = 1.436... \times 10^{-30}$ m³ $\rho_{atom} = \frac{m}{V}$ so $\rho = \dfrac{2.00 \times 10^{-26}}{1.436... \times 10^{-30}} = \mathbf{1.4 \times 10^4\ kg\,m^{-3}}$ **(to 2 s.f.)**

b) $V_{nucleus} = \frac{4}{3}\pi r^3 = 1.372... \times 10^{-43}$ m³ $\rho_{nucleus} = \frac{m}{V}$ so $\rho = \dfrac{2.00 \times 10^{-26}}{1.372... \times 10^{-43}} = \mathbf{1.5 \times 10^{17}\ kg\,m^{-3}}$ **(to 2 s.f.)**

So the nucleus is about 10^{13} times as dense as the atom as a whole.

The Strong Nuclear Force Binds Nucleons Together

The **strong nuclear force** is quite **complicated**, but here are the **main points**:

1) To **hold the nucleus together**, the strong nuclear force must be an **attractive force** that **overcomes** the **electrostatic force** (the repulsive force between the positive charges of the protons, p.46).

2) Experiments have shown that the strong nuclear force between nucleons has a **short range**. It can only hold nucleons together when they are separated by up to **a few femtometres** — the size of a **nucleus**.

3) The **strength** of the strong nuclear force between nucleons **quickly falls** beyond this distance.

4) Experiments also show that the strong nuclear force **works equally between all nucleons**. This means that the size of the force is the same whether proton-proton, neutron-neutron or proton-neutron.

5) At **very small separations**, the strong nuclear force must be **repulsive** — otherwise there would be nothing to stop it **crushing** the nucleus to a **point**.

Green, yellow, blue, orange and red — repulsive at short separations.

The Nucleus

You Can Compare the Strong Nuclear and Electrostatic Forces

The **strong nuclear force** can be plotted on a **graph** to show how it changes with the **distance of separation** between **nucleons**. If the **electrostatic force** is also plotted, you can see the **relationship** between these **two forces**.

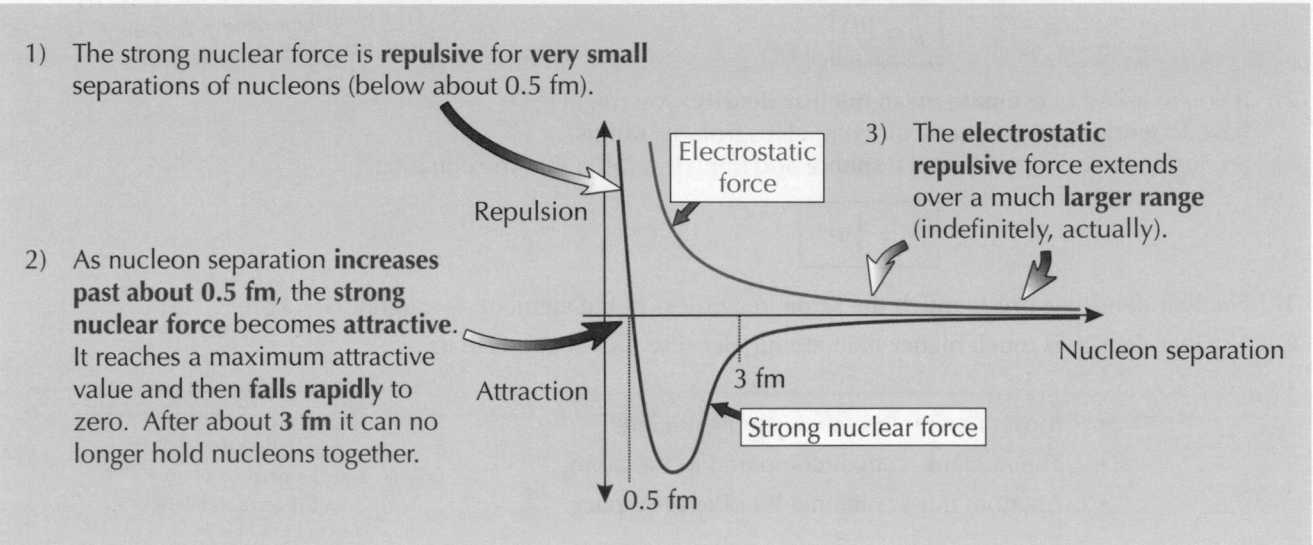

1) The strong nuclear force is **repulsive** for **very small** separations of nucleons (below about 0.5 fm).

2) As nucleon separation **increases past about 0.5 fm**, the **strong nuclear force** becomes **attractive**. It reaches a maximum attractive value and then **falls rapidly** to zero. After about **3 fm** it can no longer hold nucleons together.

3) The **electrostatic repulsive** force extends over a much **larger range** (indefinitely, actually).

Practice Questions

Q1 What is the approximate diameter of an atom? What is the approximate diameter of the smallest nucleus?

Q2 Explain why the density of atomic matter is much less than that of nuclear matter.

Q3 What causes an electrostatic force inside the nucleus?

Q4 Is the strong nuclear force attractive or repulsive at a nucleon separation of 2 fm?

Exam Questions

Q1 a) Given that $r_0 = 1.4$ fm, estimate the radius of the nucleus of an oxygen-16 atom. [1 mark]

   b) An atom of iodine has a nucleon number of 127. An atom of nitrogen has a nucleon number of 14. Estimate how many times larger the radius of an iodine nucleus is than the radius of a nitrogen nucleus. [2 marks]

Q2 A radium nucleus has a radius of 8.53×10^{-15} m and a mass of 3.75×10^{-25} kg. Estimate the mean density of the radium nucleus. [2 marks]

Q3 A sample of pure gold has a density of 19 300 kg m^{-3}. If the density of a gold nucleus is 1.47×10^{17} kg m^{-3}, discuss what this implies about the structure of a gold atom. [4 marks]

Q4 The strong nuclear force binds the nucleus together.

   a) Explain why the force must be repulsive at very short distances. [1 mark]

   b) Explain how the strong nuclear force limits the size of a stable nucleus. [2 marks]

Don't know about you, but this stuff makes me feel pretty dense...

Right then, lots of scary looking stuff on these pages, but the important bits can be condensed into a few points: a) the radius of the nucleus is directly proportional to the cube root of the nucleon number, b) nuclear density is really high compared to the atomic density, c) the strong nuclear force is repulsive for really small separations, but becomes attractive for slightly larger separations, then gets weaker as separation increases. Got that?

Classification of Particles

Time for a quick primer on particles — hope you're as excited as I am...

Hadrons are Particles that Feel the Strong Nuclear Force

1) **Not all particles** can feel **the strong nuclear force** — the ones that **can** are called **hadrons**.
2) Hadrons **aren't fundamental** particles. They're made up of **smaller particles** called **quarks** (see pages 68-69).
3) **Protons** and **neutrons** are **hadrons**. This is why they can make atomic nuclei — the nucleus of an atom is made up from protons and neutrons held together by the **strong nuclear force** (p.63).
4) As well as **protons** and **neutrons**, there are **other hadrons** that you don't get in normal matter, like **sigmas** (Σ) and **mesons** — luckily you **don't** need to know about them (woohoo!).

The Proton is the Only Stable Hadron

1) Most **hadrons** will eventually **decay** into **other particles**. The exception is protons — most physicists think that protons don't **decay**.
2) The **neutron** is an **unstable particle** that **decays** into a **proton**. (But it's much more stable when it's part of a nucleus.) It's really just an **example** of β⁻ decay (see p.72), which is caused by the **weak nuclear force**.

Some theories predict that protons should decay with a very long half-life of about 10³² years — but there's no experimental evidence for it at the moment.

$$n \rightarrow p + e^- + \bar{\nu}$$

This is an antineutrino (see p.66).

3) Free neutrons (i.e. ones not held in a nucleus) have a half-life of about 15 minutes.

Leptons Don't Feel the Strong Nuclear Force

1) **Leptons** are **fundamental particles** and they **don't** feel the **strong nuclear force**. They **interact** with other particles via the **weak nuclear force** and **gravity** (and the electromagnetic force if they're charged).
2) There are two types of lepton you need to know about — **electrons** (e⁻) which should be familiar, and **neutrinos** (ν).
3) Neutrinos have **zero** (or almost zero) **mass** and **zero electric charge** — so they don't do much. **Neutrinos** only take part in **weak interactions** (see p.69). In fact, a neutrino can **pass right through the Earth** without **anything** happening to it.

Name	Symbol	Charge (relative to e)
electron	e⁻	–1
neutrino	ν	0

ν is the Greek letter "nu".

Practice Questions

Q1 What are hadrons made up of?
Q2 Give two differences between a hadron and a lepton.
Q3 Which is the only stable hadron? Name another hadron that will decay into it.
Q4 Name two types of lepton.

Exam Questions

Q1 State the decay products of the neutron. Explain why this decay cannot be due to the strong nuclear force. [3 marks]

Q2 A particle is detected that has no charge and that does not feel the strong nuclear force. Suggest what the particle might be. [1 mark]

Go back to the top of the page — do not pass GO, do not collect £200...

There's a frankly silly number of physics words on this page, but it looks worse than it is. Honestly. Give it another read, and don't move on until you're sure you know it all, otherwise the next few pages will sound like nonsense...

Antiparticles

Antiparticles seem to laugh in the face of common sense — but actually, they help to explain a lot in particle physics...

Antiparticles were Predicted Before they were Discovered

When **Paul Dirac** wrote down an equation obeyed by **electrons**, he found a kind of **mirror image** solution.

1) It predicted the existence of a particle like the **electron** but with **opposite electric charge** — the **positron**.
2) The **positron** turned up later in a cosmic ray experiment.
   Positrons have **identical mass** to electrons but they carry a **positive** charge.

Every Particle has an Antiparticle

Each particle type has a **corresponding antiparticle** with the **same mass** but with **opposite charge**.
For instance, an **antiproton** is a **negatively charged** particle with the same mass as the **proton**.

Even the shadowy **neutrino** has an antiparticle version called the **antineutrino** — it doesn't do much either.

Particle	Symbol	Relative charge	Rest mass (kg)	Antiparticle	Symbol	Relative charge	Rest mass (kg)
proton	p	+1	1.673×10^{-27}	antiproton	$\bar{p}$	−1	1.673×10^{-27}
neutron	n	0	1.675×10^{-27}	antineutron	$\bar{n}$	0	1.675×10^{-27}
electron	e^-	−1	9.11×10^{-31}	positron	e^+	+1	9.11×10^{-31}
neutrino	ν	0	0	antineutrino	$\bar{\nu}$	0	0

1) In the exam, you'll be **given** the masses of protons, neutrons and electrons. Just remember that the mass of an **antiparticle** is the **same** as the mass of its corresponding particle.
2) The masses in the table are all **rest masses** — the mass of the particle when it's **not moving**. This is because the masses of objects change when they're moving at very high speeds, but you don't need to know about that.
3) You need to **learn** the **relative charges** on each type of particle (these are all relative to $e = 1.60 \times 10^{-19}$ C).
4) Neutrinos are **incredibly tiny** — you can assume they have zero mass and zero charge.

You can Create Matter and Antimatter from Energy

You've probably heard about the **equivalence** of energy and mass. It all comes out of Einstein's special theory of relativity. **Energy** can turn into **mass** and **mass** can turn into **energy** if you know how — all you need is one fantastic and rather famous formula:

$$\Delta E = \Delta mc^2$$

As you've probably guessed, there's a bit **more to it** than that:

When **energy** is converted into **mass** you get **equal amounts** of **matter** and **antimatter**.

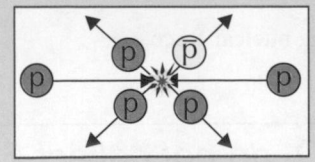

Fire **two protons** at each other at high speed and you'll end up with a lot of **energy** at the point of impact. This energy might be converted into **more particles**.

If an extra **proton** is formed then there will always be an **antiproton** to go with it. It's called **pair production**.

Antiparticles

Each *Particle-Antiparticle Pair* is Produced from a *Single Photon*

Pair production only happens if **one photon** has enough energy to produce that much mass. It also tends to happen near a **nucleus**, which helps conserve momentum.

You usually get **electron-positron** pairs produced (rather than any other pair) — because they have a relatively **low mass**.

The **minimum** amount of energy the **photon** must have is the **combined energy** of the **two** particles **at rest** (i.e. assuming that the particles have **negligible** kinetic energy).

You can calculate the **minimum** energy, E_γ, using $\Delta E = \Delta mc^2$:

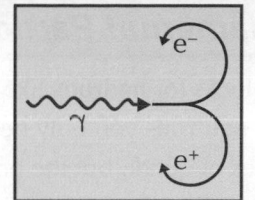

The particle tracks are curved because there's usually a magnetic field present in particle physics experiments. They curve in opposite directions because of the opposite charges on the electron and positron.

1) The **minimum energy** a photon must have to undergo pair production (E_γ) must be **equal** to the energy (at rest) of the **particles produced**.

2) A particle and its antiparticle have the **same rest mass** (m), which means that: $\implies E_\gamma = 2mc^2$

3) You can go further and find the **maximum wavelength** or **minimum frequency** of the photon using the equation for the **energy of a photon**: $\implies E_\gamma = \dfrac{hc}{\lambda} = hf$

4) Just put these two equations for E_γ together and **rearrange** to find λ or f.

The *Opposite* of *Pair Production* is *Annihilation*

When a **particle** meets its **antiparticle** the result is **annihilation**. All the **mass** of the particle and antiparticle gets converted to **energy**, in the form of a pair of photons. In ordinary matter antiparticles can only exist for a fraction of a second before this happens, so you won't see many of them.

Just like with pair production, you can calculate the **minimum energy** of each photon produced (i.e. assuming that the particles have **negligible** kinetic energy).

The combined energy of the photons will be equal to the combined energy of the particles, so $2E_\gamma = 2mc^2$ and so $\boxed{E_\gamma = mc^2}$

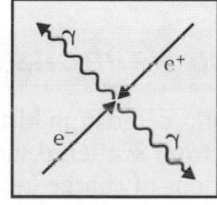

The electron and positron annihilate and their mass is converted into the energy of a pair of identical gamma ray photons.

You can calculate the minimum frequency and maximum wavelength as before.

Practice Questions

Q1 Which antiparticle has zero charge and a rest mass of 1.675×10^{-27} kg?

Q2 What is the symbol for an antineutrino?

Q3 Describe the properties of an antineutrino.

Q4 Write down the charge of a positron, given that the charge on an electron is -1.60×10^{-19} C.

Q5 Give one similarity and one difference between a proton and an antiproton.

Exam Questions

Q1 Explain why the reaction $p + p \rightarrow p + p + n$ is not possible. [1 mark]

Q2 Write down an equation for the reaction between a positron and an electron and state the name of this type of reaction. [2 marks]

Q3 Assuming both particles have negligible kinetic energy, calculate the frequency of the photons produced when a proton and an antiproton annihilate. ($m_p = 1.673 \times 10^{-27}$ kg, $h = 6.63 \times 10^{-34}$ Js, $c = 3.00 \times 10^8$ ms^{-1}) [3 marks]

Pair production — never seems to happen with my socks...

The idea of every particle having an antiparticle might seem a bit strange, but just make sure you know the main points — a) if energy is converted into a particle, you also get an antiparticle, b) an antiparticle won't last long before it bumps into the right particle and annihilates it, c) this releases the energy it took to make them to start with...

Quarks

Quarks are the fundamental particles that make up protons and neutrons. If you haven't yet, it's probably best to read pages 65–67 before you start — then this will all make a bit more sense...

Quarks are Fundamental Particles

Quarks are the **building blocks** for **hadrons** like **protons** and **neutrons**.

1) To make **protons** and **neutrons** you only need two types of quark — the **up** quark (**u**) and the **down** quark (**d**).

2) There a few more types of quark, but the only other one you need to know about is the **strange** quark (**s**).

The **antiparticles** of hadrons (like antiprotons and antineutrons) are made from **anti-quarks**.

Quarks and Anti-quarks have Opposite Charges

The **anti-quarks** have **opposite charges** to the quarks — as you'd expect.

Quarks:

name	symbol	relative charge
up	u	$+\frac{2}{3}$
down	d	$-\frac{1}{3}$
strange	s	$-\frac{1}{3}$

Anti-quarks:

name	symbol	relative charge
anti-up	$\bar{u}$	$-\frac{2}{3}$
anti-down	$\bar{d}$	$+\frac{1}{3}$
anti-strange	$\bar{s}$	$+\frac{1}{3}$

As on p.65 and p.66, these charges are relative to the elementary charge, *e*.

Protons and Neutrons are Made from Three Quarks

Evidence for quarks came from **hitting protons** with **high energy electrons**. The way the **electrons scattered** showed that there were **three concentrations of charge** (quarks) **inside** the proton.

The quarks that a particle is made up from is called its 'quark composition'.

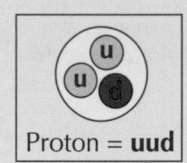

Total relative charge
$= \frac{2}{3} + \frac{2}{3} - \frac{1}{3} = 1$

Proton = **uud**

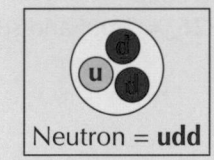

Total relative charge
$= \frac{2}{3} - \frac{1}{3} - \frac{1}{3} = 0$

Neutron = **udd**

Antiprotons are $\bar{u}\bar{u}\bar{d}$ and antineutrons are $\bar{u}\bar{d}\bar{d}$ — so no surprises there then.

Not all hadrons have **three quarks** though. Protons and neutrons are a type of hadron called **baryons**, which are made up of **three quarks**. There are also hadrons made up of a **quark** and an **anti-quark**, called **mesons** — but you don't really need to know about them.

There's no Such Thing as a Free Quark

What if you **blasted** a **proton** with **enough energy** — could you **separate out** the quarks? Nope. The energy just gets changed into more **quarks and antiquarks** — it's **pair production** again (see p.66) and it makes **mesons**.

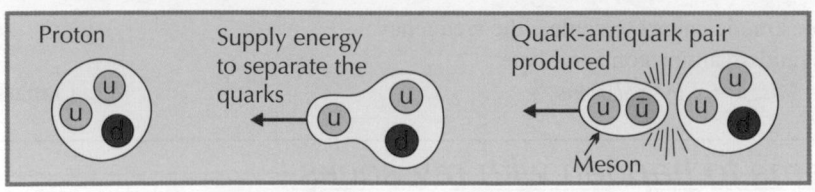

Proton   Supply energy to separate the quarks   Quark-antiquark pair produced

Meson

This is called **quark confinement**.

Quarks

The **Weak Nuclear Force** is Something that Changes the **Quark Type**

Hadrons can **decay** into other particles via the **weak nuclear force** (p.65). This is the **only thing** that can change one type of quark into another.

In **beta-minus** (β⁻) decay a **neutron** is changed into a **proton** — in other words **udd** changes into **uud**. It means turning a **d** quark into a **u** quark.

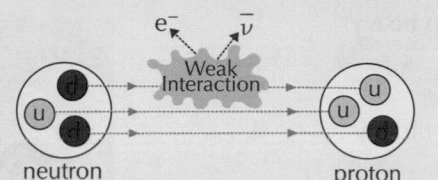

You might also see electrons and positrons written as $_{-1}^{0}e$ and $_{+1}^{0}e$

Some unstable isotopes like **carbon-11** decay by **beta-plus** (β⁺) emission. In this case a **proton** changes to a **neutron**, so a **u** quark changes to a **d** quark.

neutron → proton

in terms of **quarks**: $\quad d \rightarrow u + e^- + \bar{\nu}$

in terms of **charge**: $\quad (-\frac{1}{3}) \rightarrow (+\frac{2}{3}) + (-1) + 0$

proton → neutron

in terms of **quarks**: $\quad u \rightarrow d + e^+ + \nu$

in terms of **charge**: $\quad (+\frac{2}{3}) \rightarrow (-\frac{1}{3}) + (+1) + 0$

In any other kind of interaction, the number of quarks of **any type** must be the same before the interaction as after it. In **all** interactions, **charge must be conserved**.

Charge is Always **Conserved** in **Particle Reactions**

In **any** particle reaction, the **total charge** after the reaction must equal the total charge before the reaction.

Example: A Σ⁺ particle can decay to produce a π⁺ particle and another particle A. By considering the charge on each quark, identify the missing quark (labelled '?') in this reaction, and hence state the name of particle A.

$$\Sigma^+ \rightarrow A + \pi^+$$
$$uus \rightarrow ?dd + u\bar{d}$$

Write down the charge on each quark and then find the total charge on each particle.

u	u	s	→	?	d	d	+	u	$\bar{d}$
$+\frac{2}{3}$	$+\frac{2}{3}$	$-\frac{1}{3}$	→	?	$-\frac{1}{3}$	$-\frac{1}{3}$	+	$+\frac{2}{3}$	$+\frac{1}{3}$
		+1	→		$(? - \frac{2}{3})$		+		+1

For charge to be conserved, the missing quark must have a charge of $+\frac{2}{3}$. This means it must be an **up quark**.

This means particle A is made up of the quarks udd, so it is a **neutron**.

Practice Questions

Q1 What is a quark? Write down the quark composition of protons and neutrons.

Q2 State the relative charge of: a) a strange quark,   b) an anti-strange quark.

Q3 Explain why quarks are never observed on their own.

Q4 Write down the equation for β⁺ decay in terms of quarks.

Exam Questions

Q1 Particle interactions involving hadrons can take place via the strong nuclear force and the weak nuclear force. In which of these types of interaction is charge conserved?
   A: Strong only   B: Weak only   C: Strong and weak   D: None   [1 mark]

Q2 a) State the equation for beta-minus decay:

     i)   in terms of hadrons and leptons.   [2 marks]

     ii)   in terms of quarks and leptons.   [1 mark]

   b) Explain, in terms of the charges on quarks and leptons, how this reaction conserves charge.   [3 marks]

A quark — not the noise a posh duck makes...

Don't know about you, but I'm getting a wee bit sick of tables of particles to learn. Sadly you need to learn all this stuff, but none of it's too tricky, so make yourself a cuppa and give it all another read...

Radioactive Decay

Despite its best intentions, the strong force can't always hold nuclei together — instead you get radioactive emissions.

Unstable Nuclei are Radioactive

1) The nucleus is under the **influence** of the **strong nuclear force holding** it **together** and the **electrostatic force pushing** the **protons apart**. It's a very **delicate balance**, and it's easy for a nucleus to become **unstable**.

2) If a nucleus is **unstable**, it will **break down** to **become** more stable.
Its **instability** could be caused by:

- **too many neutrons**
- **too many nucleons** in total (it's **too heavy**)
- **too few neutrons**
- **too much energy** in the nucleus

3) The nucleus **decays** by **releasing energy** and/or **particles** (nuclear radiation), until it reaches a **stable form** — this is called **radioactive decay**.

4) An individual radioactive decay is **spontaneous** and **random** — it can't be predicted.

5) Although you can't predict the decay of an **individual nucleus**, if you take a **very large number of nuclei**, their **overall behaviour** shows a **pattern**.

6) Any sample of a particular **isotope** (p.61) has the **same rate of decay**, i.e. the same **proportion** of nuclei will **decay** in a **given time** (p.73).

This radio was
pretty active...

There are Four Types of Nuclear Radiation

You need to know all about the **four** different types of **nuclear radiation** — here's a handy **table** to get you started.

Radiation	Symbol	Constituent	Relative Charge	Mass (u)
Alpha	α	A helium nucleus — 2 protons & 2 neutrons	+2	4
Beta-minus (Beta)	β or β^-	Electron	–1	(negligible)
Beta-plus	β^+	Positron	+1	(negligible)
Gamma	γ	Short-wavelength, high-frequency electromagnetic wave.	0	0

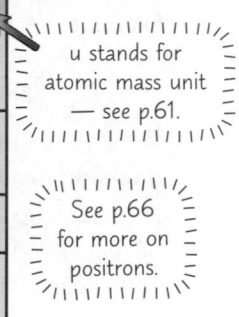

u stands for atomic mass unit — see p.61.

See p.66 for more on positrons.

The Different Types of Radiation have Different Properties

When radiation **hits** an **atom** it can **knock off electrons**, creating an **ion** — so, **radioactive emissions** are also known as **ionising radiation**. The **different types** of radiation have **different ionising powers** as well as different **speeds** and **penetrating powers**.

Radiation	Symbol	Ionising Power	Speed	Penetrating power	Affected by magnetic field
Alpha	α	Strong	Slow	Absorbed by paper or a few cm of air	Yes
Beta-minus (Beta)	β or β^-	Weak	Fast	Absorbed by ~3 mm of aluminium	Yes
Beta-plus	β^+	Annihilated by electron — so virtually zero range			
Gamma	γ	Very weak	Speed of light	Absorbed by many cm of lead, or several m of concrete	No

The **stronger** the **ionising power** of radiation, the **more energy** it **loses** in a given distance, so the **shorter** the **range** of the radiation.

Radioactive Decay

You can Investigate the Penetration of Different Kinds of Radiation in the Lab

You can investigate the penetration of different kinds of radiation by using different radioactive sources. These can be dangerous if you don't use them properly:

- Radioactive sources should be kept in a **lead-lined box** when they're not being used.
- They should only be picked up using **long-handled tongs** or **forceps**.
- Take care not to **point** them at anyone, and always keep a **safe distance** from them.

Lead will absorb all types of ionising radiation if it's thick enough.

1) Set up the equipment as shown on the right, so that when nothing is placed between the source and tube, the counter records a **high count rate**. You could instead attach the Geiger-Müller tube to a **data-logger** and a **computer** to reduce **human error**.

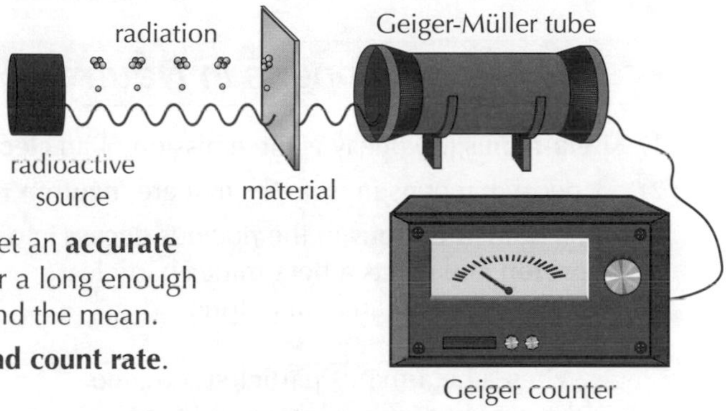

2) Remove the source and measure the **background count**. Radioactive decay is **random**, so to get an **accurate** and **precise** reading, the count needs to be measured over a long enough **time interval** (e.g. 30 seconds). Do this three times and find the mean.

3) Divide your count by this time interval to get a **background count rate**. You should subtract this from all your results.

4) Replace the source and insert **different materials** between the source and tube. Record the count rate for each material three times and find the mean.

5) If the count rate remains about **the same** when the material is inserted, then the radiation can **penetrate** the material. If the count rate **drops** by a large amount, then the radiation is being **absorbed** and blocked by the material. If the count rate drops to **zero** after the background count is subtracted, the radiation is being **completely absorbed**.

Take repeated measurements of the count rate and calculate averages to make your results more precise.

6) You can repeat this experiment with **different sources** to see how different kinds of radiation are blocked by different materials. You'll probably need to change the **distance** between the source and the Geiger-Müller tube for **each source**, as different kinds of radiation have different penetrating powers in **air** (see p.70).

If you're comparing penetration across different materials, they're unlikely to all have the same thickness. Bear this in mind when you draw your conclusions.

7) You could also adjust this experiment to investigate how the count rate for a particular source is affected by the thickness of a particular material — e.g. by using **sheets** of aluminium for beta radiation or different thicknesses of lead for gamma radiation. Or you could investigate how the count rate changes with distance between the source and the Geiger-Müller tube, and plot a **graph** of your results.

You Can Represent Nuclear Decay Using Equations

1) You usually write the particles in **standard notation** (see page 61) so you can see exactly what happens to the **protons** and **neutrons**.

2) For example, the decay of americium-241 to neptunium-237 looks like this: $\implies$ $^{241}_{95}\text{Am} \longrightarrow \, ^{237}_{93}\text{Np} + \, ^{4}_{2}\alpha$

3) Decay equations need to be **balanced** — in every nuclear reaction, including fission and fusion (p.78-79), **charge** and **nucleon number** must be **conserved**.

4) In this example, there are 241 nucleons **before** the decay (in the americium-241 atom), and 241 nucleons **after** the decay (237 in the neptunium-237 atom and 4 in the alpha particle), so **nucleon number** is conserved.

5) You can see that **charge** is conserved by looking at the **proton number** (the blue numbers in the example above) — there are 95 protons before the decay and 95 after it.

6) Some particles have a **negative** charge. E.g. beta-minus particles are written with a **negative proton number** ($^{0}_{-1}\beta$).

7) **Energy** and **momentum** are also conserved in **all** nuclear reactions. Mass, however, **doesn't** have to be **conserved** — the mass of an alpha particle is **less** than the **individual masses** of **two protons** and **two neutrons**. The difference in mass is called the **mass defect** (p.76), and the **energy released** when the nucleons **bond together** to form the alpha particle accounts for the missing mass. More on that later.

Radioactive Decay

α *Emission Happens in Heavy Nuclei*

1) **Alpha emission** only happens from the nuclei of **very heavy** atoms like **uranium** and **radium**.

2) The **nuclei** of these atoms are **too massive** to be stable.

> When an alpha particle is emitted, the **proton number decreases** by **two**, and the **nucleon number decreases** by **four**.

Example: $238 = 234 + 4$ — nucleon numbers balance

$$^{238}_{92}U \longrightarrow\ ^{234}_{90}Th + ^{4}_{2}\alpha$$

$92 = 90 + 2$ — proton numbers balance, so charge is conserved

β⁻ *Emission Happens in Neutron-Rich Nuclei*

1) **Beta-minus** (β⁻) decay is the emission of an **electron** from the **nucleus** along with an **antineutrino** (p.66).

2) β⁻ decay happens in isotopes that are **'neutron rich'** (have many more **neutrons** than **protons** in their nucleus).

3) One of the **neutrons** in the nucleus **decays** into a **proton** and ejects a beta-minus particle (an electron) and an antineutrino.

> When a beta-minus particle is emitted, the **proton number increases** by **one**, and the **nucleon number stays the same**.

Example: $188 = 188 + 0 + 0$ — nucleon numbers balance

$$^{188}_{75}Re \longrightarrow\ ^{188}_{76}Os + ^{0}_{-1}\beta + ^{0}_{0}\overline{\nu}$$

$75 = 76 - 1 + 0$ — proton numbers balance charge is conserved

In **beta-plus emission**, a **proton** gets **changed** into a **neutron**, releasing a **positron** and a **neutrino**. The **proton number decreases** by **one**, and the **nucleon number stays the same**.

Example: $18 = 18 + 0 + 0$

$$^{18}_{9}F \longrightarrow\ ^{18}_{8}O + ^{0}_{+1}\overline{\beta} + ^{0}_{0}\nu$$

$9 = 8 + 1 + 0$

γ *Radiation is Emitted from Nuclei with Too Much Energy*

Gamma rays can be emitted from a nucleus with **excess energy** — we say the nucleus is **excited**. This energy is **lost** by emitting a **gamma ray**. This often happens after an **alpha** or **beta** decay has occurred.

> During **gamma emission**, there is **no change** to the nuclear **constituents** — the nucleus just **loses excess energy**.

Practice Questions

Q1 What could make a nucleus unstable?

Q2 What is meant by the statement 'radioactive decay is random'?

Q3 What are the four types of nuclear radiation? What does each one consist of?

Q4 Which type of radiation is the most penetrating? Which is the most ionising?

Q5 Describe the changes that happen in the nucleus during alpha, beta-minus, beta-plus and gamma decay.

Q6 Copy and complete the following equation for beta-plus decay: $^{10}_{6}C \rightarrow\ ^{10}_{5}B + \boxed{}\boxed{} + \boxed{}\boxed{}$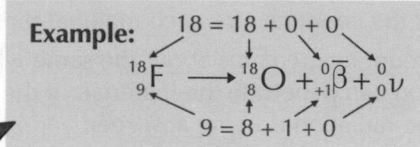

Exam Questions

Q1* A source is known to emit a single type of radiation (alpha, beta-minus or gamma).
Describe an experiment to identify the type of radiation that the source emits. [6 marks]

Q2 a) Radium-226 (Ra, proton number 88) decays to radon (Rn) by emitting an alpha particle.
Write a balanced nuclear equation for this reaction. [3 marks]

b) Potassium-40 (K, proton number 19) decays to calcium (Ca) by emitting an electron.
Write a balanced nuclear equation for this reaction. [3 marks]

*The quality of your extended response will be assessed in this question.

Radioactive emissions — as easy as α, β, γ...

You need to learn the different types of nuclear radiation and their properties, and how to write equations for all the different types of decay. Just remember that charge and nucleon number are conserved, and you won't go far wrong...

Exponential Law of Decay

Different radioactive isotopes emit radiation at different rates. Enter the decay constant and his sidekick half-life...

The **Rate of Radioactive Decay** is Measured by the **Decay Constant**

Radioactive decay is random (p.70), but for any radioactive sample, you can **predict** how many nuclei will decay in a given amount of time. The **activity** — the **number** of nuclei that **decay each second** — is **proportional** to the **size of the sample**. For a **given isotope**, **twice** the **number** of nuclei will decay per second in a sample **twice** as **large**.

The **decay constant** (λ) measures how **quickly** an isotope will **decay** — the **bigger** the value of λ, the faster the rate of decay. Its unit is s^{-1}.

| **activity = decay constant × number of undecayed nuclei** | In symbols: | $A = \lambda N$ |

Don't get λ confused with wavelength.

Activity is measured in **becquerels** (Bq). An activity of 1 Bq means that 1 nucleus decays per second (s^{-1}).

Because the activity, A, is the number of nuclei that decay each second, you can write it as the **change** in the number of undecayed nuclei, ΔN, during a **given time** (in seconds), Δt: $\Rightarrow$

$$A = -\frac{\Delta N}{\Delta t}$$

There's a minus sign in this equation because ΔN is always a **decrease**.

Combining these two equations for the activity then gives the **rate of change** of the number of undecayed nuclei:

$$-\frac{\Delta N}{\Delta t} = \lambda N$$

$\frac{\Delta N}{\Delta t}$ = rate of change of number of undecayed nuclei, N = number of undecayed nuclei in sample, λ = decay constant

Example: A sample of a radioactive isotope contains 3.0×10^{19} nuclei.
Its activity is measured to be 2.4×10^{12} Bq.
Calculate the isotope's decay constant.

Rearrange $A = \lambda N$ to give: $\lambda = A/N = (2.4 \times 10^{12}) \div (3.0 \times 10^{19}) = \mathbf{8.0 \times 10^{-8}\ s^{-1}}$

Sometimes you might be given N in mols (p.9). Remember that 1 mol contains 6.02×10^{23} nuclei.

You can **Model Radioactive Decay** using a **Spreadsheet**

Radioactive decay is an **iterative** process (the number of nuclei that decay in one time period controls the number that are available to decay in the next). This means that you can use a **spreadsheet** to model how a sample of an isotope will decay if you know the **decay constant**, λ, and the **number of undecayed nuclei** in the initial sample, N_0:

1) Set up a spreadsheet with column headings for **total time** (*t*), ΔN and N, and a data input cell for each of Δt and λ.

2) Decide on a Δt that you want to use — this is the **time interval** between the values of N that the spreadsheet will calculate. The most sensible time interval will depend on your decay constant.

If you write the formulas properly, the spreadsheet can automatically fill them in for as many rows (iterations) as you want.

3) You can then enter formulas into the spreadsheet to calculate the number of undecayed nuclei left in the sample after each time interval. You'll need to use $\Delta N = -\lambda \times N \times \Delta t$ (rearranged from the purple box above).

$\lambda\ (s^{-1})$ = e.g. 1×10^{-4}

$\Delta t\ (s)$ = e.g. 1000

Be careful when you refer to these in your formulas — make sure the cell references don't change when you autofill in new rows (iterations).

t in s	ΔN (from equation above)	N
$t_0 = 0$		N_0 = initial number of nuclei in sample
$t_1 = t_0 + \Delta t$	$(\Delta N)_1 = -\lambda \times N_0 \times \Delta t$	$N_1 = N_0 + (\Delta N)_1$
$t_2 = t_1 + \Delta t$	$(\Delta N)_2 = -\lambda \times N_1 \times \Delta t$	$N_2 = N_1 + (\Delta N)_2$
$t_3 = ...$	$(\Delta N)_3 = ...$	$N_3 = ...$

4) If you plot a graph of the number of undecayed nuclei against time, it should look like this: (You may have to fiddle with your value for Δt to get a graph with a nice shape.) This is an **exponential** graph, and there's more about it coming up on the next few pages. (See p.88-89 for more on exponential functions.)

5) You can also simulate radioactive decay using **dice**. The dice represent undecayed nuclei and if they land on a particular number, say 6, they have 'decayed'. Record how many dice you start with (you'll need quite a few) and throw them all, removing any that 'decay', then throw the rest again. Your results of the number of dice remaining against time should show the same pattern.

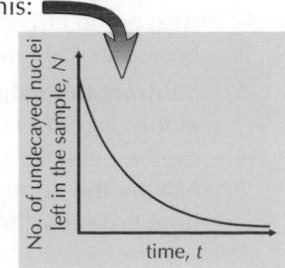

No. of undecayed nuclei left in the sample, N — time, t

Exponential Law of Decay

You Need to **Learn** the **Definition of Half-Life**

The **half-life** ($t_{1/2}$) of an **isotope** is the **average time** it takes for the **number of undecayed nuclei** to **halve**.

Measuring the **number of undecayed nuclei** isn't the easiest job in the world. **In practice**, half-life isn't measured by counting nuclei, but by measuring the **time it takes** the **activity** or **count rate** to **halve**.

The **longer** the **half-life** of an isotope, the **longer** it stays **radioactive**.

The count rate is the number of decays detected per second (it's lower than the activity).

The **Number** of **Undecayed** Nuclei **Decreases Exponentially**

You **can't** tell when any **one nucleus** is going to **decay**, but you can **predict** how many nuclei will decay in a given time period by generating a **graph** like the one on the previous page, shown again below.

You can use this **graph** to find the **half-life** of an isotope:

1) Read off the number of undecayed nuclei when $t = 0$.

2) Go to half the original value of N.

3) Draw a horizontal line to the curve, then a vertical line down to the x-axis.

4) The half-life is where this line meets the x-axis.

5) It's always a good idea to check your answer. Repeat steps 1-3 for a quarter of the original value of N, and divide the time where the line meets the x-axis by two. That will also give you the half-life. You can do the same for an eighth of the original value (divide the time by 3), and a sixteenth of the original value. Check that you get the same answer each way.

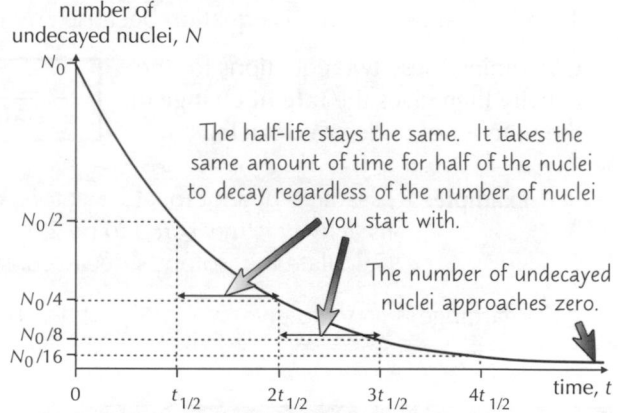

number of undecayed nuclei, N

The half-life stays the same. It takes the same amount of time for half of the nuclei to decay regardless of the number of nuclei you start with.

The number of undecayed nuclei approaches zero.

You can Generate a **Count-Rate** Decay Graph **Experimentally**

You're most likely to do this using the isotope **protactinium-234**.

Protactinium-234 is formed when **uranium** decays (via another isotope). You can measure protactinium-234's decay rate using a **protactinium generator** — a bottle containing a uranium salt, the decay products of uranium (including protactinium-234) and two solvents, which separate out into layers, like this:

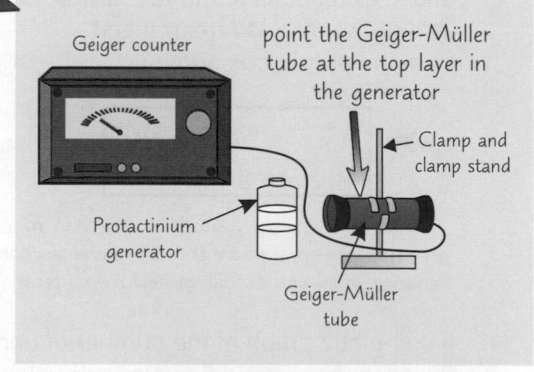

layer containing protactinium-234

layer containing uranium salt

1) **Shake the bottle** to mix the solvents together, then add it to the equipment shown on the right.

2) Wait for the liquids to **separate**. The protactinium-234 will be in solution in the top layer, and the uranium salt will stay in the bottom layer. Then you can point the Geiger-Müller tube at the top layer to measure the activity of the protactinium-234.

3) As soon as the liquids separate, record the count rate (e.g. how many counts you get in 10 seconds). Re-measure the count rate at sensible intervals (e.g. every 30 seconds).

4) Once you've collected your data, leave the bottle to stand for at least ten minutes, then take the count rate again. This is the **background count rate** corresponding to background radiation (you could also do this at the beginning of the experiment, before shaking the bottle).

5) **Subtract this value** from your measured count rates, then plot a graph of count rate against time. It should look like the graph on the right. You can use this graph to find the **half-life** in exactly the same way as above. In this case the half-life is the time taken for the count rate (or activity) to halve.

Geiger counter

point the Geiger-Müller tube at the top layer in the generator

Clamp and clamp stand

Protactinium generator

Geiger-Müller tube

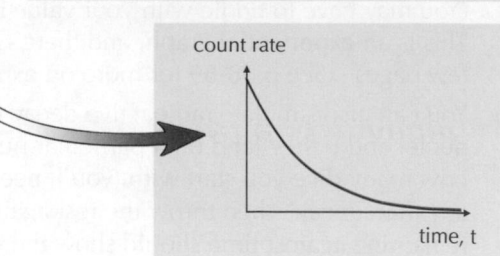

count rate

time, t

Exponential Law of Decay

You Need to Know the *Equations* for *Half-Life* and *Decay*

1) It won't surprise you to know that you can also calculate an isotope's **half-life** mathematically. The equation for calculating half-life is:

$$\lambda t_{1/2} = \ln 2$$

Where ln is the natural log (p.88), λ is the decay constant in s^{-1}, and $t_{1/2}$ is the half-life in seconds.

2) As you know, the **number of undecayed nuclei remaining**, N, depends on the **number originally present**, N_0, the **decay constant**, λ, and how much **time** has passed, t. There's an equation for this, too:

Here t = time, measured in seconds.

$$N = N_0 e^{-\lambda t}$$

This is the equation of the line generated from the spreadsheet on page 73.

3) Finally, there's an equation for how a sample's **activity** goes down as it decays:

$$A = A_0 e^{-\lambda t}$$

A is the activity at time t, and A_0 is the initial activity (at $t = 0$ s). Both are measured in Bq.

Radioactive Isotopes can be used to *Date Objects*

The radioactive isotope **carbon-14** is used in **radioactive dating**:

1) Living plants take in carbon dioxide from the atmosphere as part of **photosynthesis**, including the **radioactive isotope carbon-14**. Animals then take this carbon-14 in when they eat the plants. All living things contain the **same percentage** of carbon-14.

2) When they die, the **activity** of carbon-14 in the plant starts to **fall**, with a **half-life** of around **5730 years**.

3) Archaeological finds made from once-living material (like wood) can be tested to find the **current amount** of carbon-14 in them. This can be used to calculate how long the material has been dead for — i.e. how old it is.

According to the latest scientific techniques, Ron's moustache dated back to the early 1980s.

Practice Questions

Q1 Define radioactive activity. Write down an equation relating activity and the number of undecayed nuclei.

Q2 Describe how you could model radioactive decay using a spreadsheet (and if you have a computer handy, have a go at doing it for a sample of 200 000 nuclei with a decay constant of 0.002 s^{-1}).

Q3 Describe how dice could be used to simulate radioactive decay.

Q4 Sketch a general radioactive decay graph showing the activity against time and write an equation for the relationship.

Q5 Define the term 'half life'. Describe an experiment to measure the half-life of protactinium-234.

Q6 Explain how radioactive dating works.

Exam Question

Q1 A scientist takes a reading of 750 Bq from a pure radioactive source. The radioactive source initially contains 50 000 undecayed nuclei, and background activity in the lab is measured as 50 Bq.

a) Calculate the decay constant for the sample. [2 marks]

b) Calculate the half-life of the sample. [1 mark]

c) Calculate how many undecayed nuclei of the radioactive source will be left after 300 seconds. [1 mark]

Radioactivity is a random process — just like revision shouldn't be...

Remember the shape of that graph — whether it's count rate, activity or number of nuclei plotted against time, the shape's always the same. The maths is a bit of a pain, but I think the experiment's pretty good. Protactinium generator, sounds like something out of a film that's on at 2 o'clock in the morning...

Binding Energy

Turn off the radio and close the door, 'cos you're going to need to concentrate hard on this stuff about binding energy...

The **Mass Defect** is **Equivalent** to the **Binding Energy**

1) The **mass** of a **nucleus** is **less than** the mass of its **constituent parts** — the difference is called the **mass defect**. Mass and energy are **equivalent**, according to Einstein's equation:

$$\Delta E = \Delta m c^2$$

ΔE is the energy released in J
Δm is the mass defect in kg
c is the speed of light in a vacuum

2) As nucleons join together, the total mass **decreases** — this '**lost**' mass is **converted** into energy and **released**. You can calculate this energy using the equation above.

3) The amount of **energy released** is **equivalent** to the **mass defect**.

4) If you **pulled** the nucleus completely **apart**, the **energy** you'd have to use to do it would be the **same** as the energy **released** when the nucleus formed.

> The energy needed to **separate** all of the nucleons in a nucleus is called the **binding energy** (measured in **MeV**), and it is **equivalent** to the **mass defect**.

Atomic mass is usually given in atomic mass units (u), where $1\ u = 1.661 \times 10^{-27}$ kg.

Example: Calculate the binding energy of the nucleus of a lithium atom, ^6_3Li, given that its mass defect is 0.0343 u.

1) Convert the mass defect into kg: Mass defect = $0.0343 \times (1.661 \times 10^{-27}) = 5.69723 \times 10^{-29}$ kg

2) Use $\Delta E = \Delta m c^2$ to calculate the binding energy: $\Delta E = (5.69723 \times 10^{-29}) \times (3.00 \times 10^8)^2 = 5.127507 \times 10^{-12}$ J

3) Convert your answer into electron volts: $5.127507 \times 10^{-12} \div 1.60 \times 10^{-19} = 32046918.75$ eV

$1\ eV = 1.60 \times 10^{-19}$ J ⟶ **= 32.0 MeV (to 3 s.f.)**

5) The **binding energy per unit of mass defect** can also be calculated. Using the example above:

6) This means that a mass defect of **1 u** is equivalent to about **930 MeV** (to 2 s.f.) of binding energy.

$$\frac{\textbf{binding energy}}{\textbf{mass defect}} = \frac{32\ \text{MeV}}{0.0343\ \text{u}} \approx \textbf{930 MeV u}^{-1} \textbf{ (to 2 s.f.)}$$

The **Binding Energy Per Nucleon** is at a **Maximum** around **N = 50**

A useful way of **comparing** the binding energies of different nuclei is to look at the **binding energy per nucleon**.

$$\textbf{Binding energy per nucleon (in MeV)} = \frac{\textbf{Binding energy } (B)}{\textbf{Nucleon number } (A)}$$

So, the binding energy per nucleon for ^6_3Li (in the example above) is $32 \div 6 = 5.3$ MeV.

1) If you plot a **graph** of **binding energy per nucleon** against **nucleon number**, for all elements, the line of best fit shows a **curve**. A **high** binding energy per nucleon means that **more energy** is needed to **remove** nucleons from the nucleus.

2) In other words the **most stable** nuclei occur around the **maximum point** on the graph — which is at **nucleon number 56** (i.e. **iron**, Fe).

3) **Combining small nuclei** is called nuclear **fusion** (p.79) — this **increases** the **binding energy per nucleon** dramatically, which means a lot of **energy is released** during nuclear fusion.

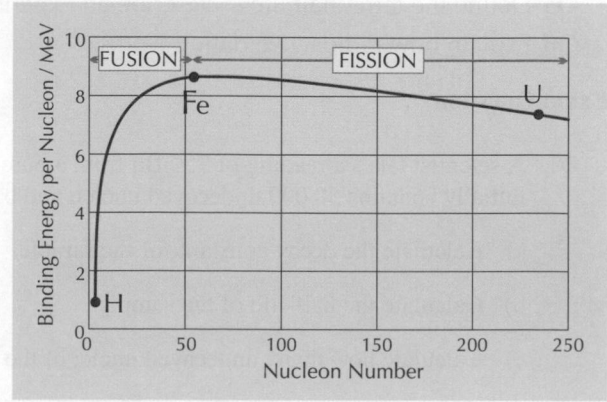

4) **Fission** is when **large nuclei** are **split in two** (see p.78) — the **nucleon numbers** of the two **new nuclei** are **smaller** than the original nucleus, which means there is an **increase** in the binding energy per nucleon. So, energy is also **released** during nuclear fission (but not as much energy per nucleon as in nuclear fusion).

Binding Energy

The *Change* in *Binding Energy* Gives the *Energy Released*

The **binding energy per nucleon graph** can be used to **estimate** the **energy released** from nuclear reactions.

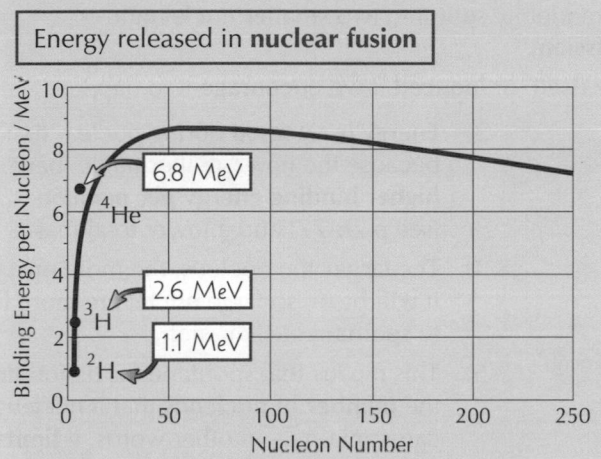

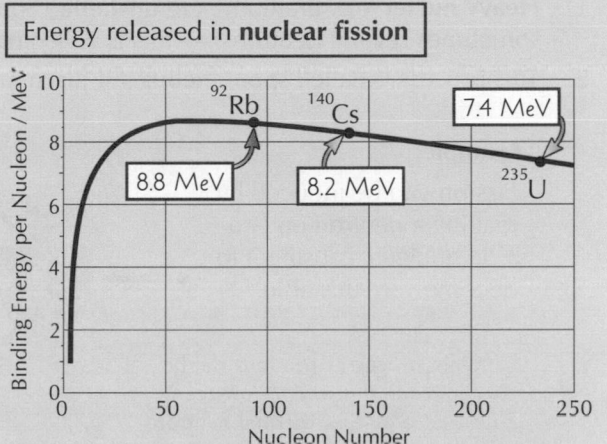

If ^{2}H and ^{3}H nuclei **fuse** together to form ^{4}He (and a neutron):

1) The binding energy before the fusion is:
   binding energy ^{2}H + binding energy ^{3}H
   $= (2 \times 1.1) + (3 \times 2.6) = \textbf{10 MeV}$

2) The binding energy after the fusion is:
   binding energy ^{4}He $= 4 \times 6.8 = \textbf{27.2 MeV}$

3) So the **energy released** is:
   $27.2 - 10 = 17.2 = \textbf{17 MeV (to 2 s.f.)}$

If a ^{235}U nucleus **splits** into ^{92}Rb and ^{140}Cs (plus a few neutrons) during nuclear **fission**:

1) The binding energy **before** the fission is:
   binding energy ^{235}U $= 235 \times 7.4 = \textbf{1739 MeV}$

2) The binding energy **after** the fission is:
   binding energy ^{92}Rb + binding energy ^{140}Cs
   $= (92 \times 8.8) + (140 \times 8.2) = \textbf{1957.6 MeV}$

3) So the **energy released** is:
   $1957.6 - 1739 = 218.6$
   $= \textbf{220 MeV (to 2 s.f.)}$

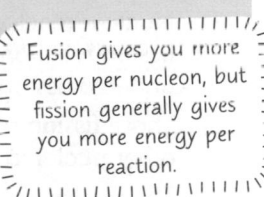

Fusion gives you more energy per nucleon, but fission generally gives you more energy per reaction.

Practice Questions

Q1 What is the binding energy of a nucleus?

Q2 How can you calculate the binding energy for a particular nucleus?

Q3 Sketch a graph of binding energy per nucleon against nucleon number, labelling the regions where fusion and fission occur and the element with the highest binding energy per nucleon.

Q4 Do nuclear fusion or fission reactions release more energy per nucleon?

Exam Questions

Q1 The mass of a $^{14}_{6}$C nucleus is 13.999948 u.
    The mass of a proton is 1.007276 u, and the mass of a neutron is 1.008665 u.

a) Calculate the mass defect of a $^{14}_{6}$C nucleus. Give your answer in atomic mass units. [2 marks]

b) Calculate the binding energy of the nucleus in MeV. [3 marks]

Q2 The following equation shows a nuclear reaction between two deuterium ($^2_1$H) nuclei, to form helium-3 ($^3_2$He):

$$^2_1\text{H} + {}^2_1\text{H} \rightarrow {}^3_2\text{He} + {}^1_0\text{n} + \text{energy}$$

a) State what type of nuclear reaction this is. [1 mark]

b) The binding energy per nucleon is 0 MeV for a neutron, approximately 1.11 MeV for a $^2_1$H nucleus, and approximately 2.58 MeV for a $^3_2$He nucleus.
    Use these values to calculate the energy released by this reaction. [3 marks]

Don't tie yourself up in knots...

This stuff is a bit of a headache — the idea of a particle having a smaller mass than the particles inside it confuses me no end — but you need to know it. You know the drill by now, back to the top of page 76, and read it all again...

Nuclear Fission and Fusion

What did the nuclear scientist have for his tea? Fission chips... hohoho.

Fission Means Splitting Up into Smaller Parts

1) **Heavy nuclei** (e.g. uranium), are **unstable**. Some can randomly **split** into two **smaller** nuclei (and sometimes several neutrons) — this is called **nuclear fission**.

2) This process is called **spontaneous** if it just happens **by itself**, or **induced** if we **encourage** it to happen.

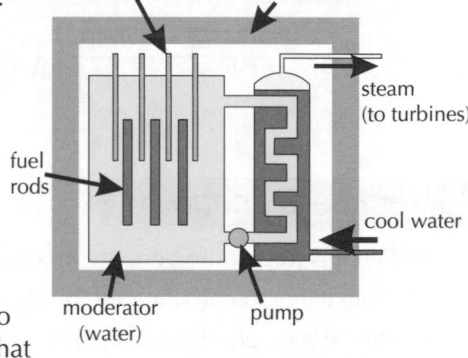

Example:

Fission can be induced by making a neutron enter a ^{235}U nucleus, causing it to become very unstable.

Only low energy neutrons can be captured in this way. A low energy neutron is called a **thermal neutron**.

3) **Energy is released** during nuclear fission because the new, smaller nuclei have a **higher binding energy per nucleon** (see p.76-77) and a lower total mass.

4) The **larger** the nucleus, the more **unstable** it will be — so large nuclei are **more likely** to **spontaneously fission**.

5) This means that spontaneous fission **limits** the **number of nucleons** that a nucleus can contain — in other words, it **limits** the number of **possible elements**.

Controlled Nuclear Reactors Produce Useful Power

We can **harness** the **energy** released during nuclear **fission reactions** in a **nuclear reactor**, but it's important that these reactions are very **carefully controlled**.

1) Nuclear reactors use **rods of uranium** that are rich in ^{235}U as 'fuel' for fission reactions. (The rods also contain a lot of ^{238}U, but that doesn't undergo fission.)

2) These **fission** reactions produce more **neutrons** which then **induce** other nuclei to fission — this is called a **chain reaction**.

3) The **neutrons** will only cause a chain reaction if they are **slowed down**, which allows them to be **captured** by the uranium nuclei — these slowed down neutrons are called **thermal neutrons**.

4) ^{235}U **fuel rods** need to be placed in a **moderator** (for example, **water**) to **slow down** and/or absorb **neutrons**. You need to choose a moderator that will slow down some neutrons enough so they can cause **further fission**, keeping the reaction going at a steady rate.

5) You want the chain reaction to continue on its own at a **steady rate**, where **one** fission follows another. The amount of 'fuel' you need to do this is called the **critical mass** — any less than the critical mass (**sub-critical mass**) and the reaction will just peter out. Nuclear reactors use a **supercritical** mass of fuel (where several new fissions normally follow each fission) and **control the rate of fission** using **control rods**.

6) Control rods control the **chain reaction** by **limiting** the number of **neutrons** in the reactor. They **absorb neutrons** so that the **rate of fission** is controlled. **Control rods** are made up of a material that **absorbs neutrons** (e.g. boron), and they can be inserted by varying amounts to control the reaction rate.
In an **emergency**, the reactor will be **shut down** automatically by the **release of the control rods** into the reactor, which will stop the reaction as quickly as possible.

7) **Coolant** is sent around the reactor to **remove heat** produced in the fission — often the coolant is the **same water** that is being used in the reactor as a **moderator**. The **heat** from the reactor can then be used to make **steam** for powering **electricity-generating turbines**.

> If the chain reaction in a nuclear reactor is **left to continue unchecked**, large amounts of **energy** are **released** in a very **short time**.
>
> **Many new fissions** will follow each fission, causing a **runaway reaction** which could lead to an **explosion**. This is what happens in a **fission (atomic) bomb**.

Nuclear Fission and Fusion

There are Costs and Benefits to Nuclear Fission Power Plants

1) Deciding whether or not to build a **nuclear power station** (and if so, **where** to build it) is a tricky business.

2) Nuclear fission doesn't produce carbon dioxide, unlike burning **fossil fuels**, so it doesn't contribute to **global warming**. It also provides a **continuous energy supply**, unlike many renewable sources (e.g. wind/solar).

3) However, some of the **waste products** of **nuclear fission** are **highly radioactive** and difficult to handle and store.

4) When material is removed from the reactor, it is initially **very hot**, so it is placed in **cooling ponds** until the **temperature falls** to a safe level. The radioactive waste is then **stored in sealed containers** in specialist facilities until its **activity has fallen** sufficiently. This can take **many years**, and there's a risk that material could escape from these containers. A leak of radioactive material could be **harmful** to the environment and local human populations both now and in the future, particularly if the material contaminated **water supplies**.

5) **Accidents** or **natural disasters** pose a risk to nuclear reactors. In 2011 an earthquake and subsequent tsunami in Japan caused a meltdown at the Fukushima nuclear power plant. Over **100 000 people** were evacuated from the area, and many tonnes of contaminated water leaked into the sea. The **perceived risk** of this kind of disaster leads many people to oppose the construction of nuclear power plants near their homes.

6) Because of all of the necessary safety precautions, **building** and **decommissioning** nuclear power plants is very **time-consuming** and **expensive**.

Fusion Means Joining Nuclei Together

1) **Two light nuclei** can **combine** to create a larger nucleus. This is called **nuclear fusion.**

2) Nuclei can **only fuse** if they have enough energy to overcome the **electrostatic** (Coulomb) **repulsion** between them (p.46), and get close enough for the **strong interaction** to bind them.

3) This means fusion reactions require **much higher temperatures** than fission, as well as high pressures (or high densities). Under such conditions, generally only found inside stars, matter turns into a state called a **plasma**.

4) A lot of **energy** is released during nuclear fusion because the new, heavier nucleus has a **much higher binding energy per nucleon** (and so a lower total mass, see p.76). The energy released helps to **maintain the high temperatures** needed for further fusion reactions.

5) Although the energy released per reaction is generally **lower** in nuclear fusion than fission (see p.77), the nuclei used in fusion have a **lower mass**, so a mole of the reactants in a fusion reaction weighs less than a mole of the reactants in a fission reaction (p.9). Gram for gram, fusion can release **more energy** than fission.

6) Scientists are trying to develop fusion reactors so that we can generate nuclear **electricity** without the waste you get from fission reactors, but they haven't yet succeeded in creating one that makes more electricity than it uses.

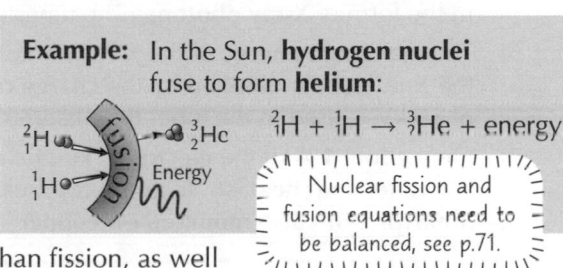

Example: In the Sun, **hydrogen nuclei** fuse to form **helium**:

$$^2_1H + ^1_1H \rightarrow ^3_2He + energy$$

Nuclear fission and fusion equations need to be balanced, see p.71.

Practice Questions

Q1 What is meant by the term 'induced fission'?

Q2 Explain what is meant by the expressions 'chain reaction', 'fuel rods' and 'moderator' in terms of nuclear fission.

Q3 What are the similarities and differences between nuclear fusion and fission?

Exam Questions

Q1 Nuclear reactors use carefully controlled chain reactions to produce energy.

   a) Describe and explain one feature of a nuclear reactor whose role is to control the rate of fission. Include an example of a suitable material for the feature you have chosen.   [3 marks]

   b) Explain what happens in a nuclear reactor during an emergency shut-down.   [2 marks]

Q2 Discuss two advantages and two disadvantages of using nuclear fission to produce electricity.   [4 marks]

If anyone asks, I've gone fission... that joke never gets old...

So, controlled nuclear fission reactions can provide a shedload of energy to generate electricity without producing pesky carbon dioxide, but nuclear energy has costs and risks too... Nothing's ever simple, is it?

X-Ray Imaging

X-ray imaging is one kind of non-invasive diagnostic technique — these techniques let doctors see what's going on (or going wrong) inside your body, without having to open you up and have a look.

X-rays are Produced by Bombarding Tungsten with High Energy Electrons

X-ray tubes are an electrical circuit, with a **cathode** (where electrons are emitted) and an **anode** (the target metal).

1) At the **cathode**, electrons are **emitted** (boiled off) by the **hot filament**.

2) This filament is **heated** by passing a **current** through it. This current is **not** the same as the current going through the **entire X-ray tube**.

3) The cathode is usually in a **cup shape**, to **focus** the **beam** of electrons onto the **target metal**.

4) The **target metal** (tungsten) acts as the **anode** of the circuit, and the **high potential difference** across the tube (**tube voltage**) causes the electrons to **accelerate** towards it.

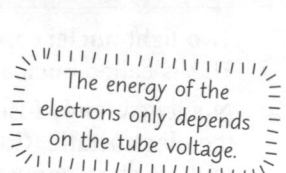

high voltage power supply, *lead shield*, *tungsten anode*, *beam of electrons*, *motor*, *evacuated glass tube*, *focusing cathode*, **X-rays**

5) When the **electrons** smash into the **tungsten anode**, they **decelerate** and some of their **kinetic energy** is converted into **electromagnetic energy**, in the form of **X-ray photons**. The tungsten anode emits a **continuous spectrum** of **X-ray radiation**.

6) The **maximum energy** of the X-ray photons is equal to the **potential difference** of the X-ray tube multiplied by the **charge** of an electron. So, if a potential difference of 50 kV is used in the tube, the maximum X-ray energy will be 50 keV.

7) Only about **1%** of the electrons' **kinetic energy** is converted into **X-rays**. The rest is converted into **heat**, so, to avoid overheating, the tungsten anode is **rotated** at about 3000 rpm. It's also **mounted** on **copper** — this **conducts** the heat away effectively.

The energy of the electrons only depends on the tube voltage.

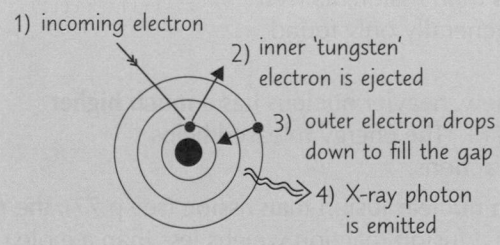

1) incoming electron
2) inner 'tungsten' electron is ejected
3) outer electron drops down to fill the gap
4) X-ray photon is emitted

- X-rays are also produced when beam electrons **knock out** other electrons from the **inner shells** of the **tungsten atoms**.

- Electrons in the atoms' **outer shells** move into the **vacancies** in the **lower energy levels**, and **release energy** in the form of **X-ray photons**.

Example: An electron hitting an anode in an X-ray tube produces maximum energy X-rays with a wavelength of 5.0×10^{-11} m. The tube voltage is halved but all other factors are kept the same. Calculate the new wavelength of the maximum energy X-rays.

The maximum energy of the electrons is $E = e \times V$, so halving the voltage would halve the maximum energy of the electrons and hence halve the maximum energy of the X-ray photons.

Since the energy of a photon $= E = \dfrac{hc}{\lambda}$, halving the energy would double the minimum wavelength.

So the new wavelength is $2 \times 5.0 \times 10^{-11} = \mathbf{1.0 \times 10^{-10}}$ **m**.

You met the equation for the energy of a photon in year 1 of A-level.

Beam Intensity is Power per Unit Area

The **intensity** of the X-ray beam is the **power** (energy per second) **per unit area** passing through a surface (at right angles). There are two ways to increase the **intensity** of the X-ray beam:

1) Increase the **tube voltage**. This gives the electrons **more kinetic energy**. Higher energy electrons can **knock out** electrons from shells **deeper** within the tungsten atoms.

2) Increase the **current** supplied to the filament. As the current increases, the **filament temperature** rises. This liberates **more electrons per second** (with the **same final energy per electron** as before), which then produce **more X-ray photons per second**.

Charlotte thought landing on her head would get top marks for beam intensity.

X-Ray Imaging

X-rays are Attenuated when they Pass Through Matter

When X-rays pass through matter (e.g. a patient's body), they are **absorbed** and **scattered**. The intensity (I) of the X-ray beam **decreases** (attenuates) **exponentially** with **distance from** the **surface** (x), according to the material's attenuation (absorption) coefficient (μ), as the equation on the right shows.

$$I = I_0 e^{-\mu x}$$

Where I_0 is the initial intensity (usually measured in Wm^{-2}), μ has units cm^{-1}, and x is measured in cm.

X-rays are Absorbed More by Bone than Soft Tissue

X-rays are **attenuated** by **absorption** and **scattering**. **Three causes** of this are:

1) The **photoelectric effect** — a **photon** with around **30 keV** of energy is absorbed by an **electron**, which is **ejected** from its atom. The gap in the **electron shell** is filled by another **electron**, which emits a **photon**.

2) **Compton scattering** — a **photon** with around **0.5-5 MeV** of energy knocks an **electron** out of an **atom**, which causes the **photon** to **lose energy** and be **scattered**.

3) **Pair production** — a high (> 1.1 MeV) **energy** photon **decays** into an **electron** and a **positron**.

How much **energy is absorbed** by a **material** depends on its **atomic number** — so tissues containing atoms with **different atomic numbers** (e.g. **soft tissue** and **bone**) will **contrast** in the X-ray image.

If the tissues in the region of interest have similar attenuation coefficients then artificial **contrast media** can be used — e.g. **barium meal** or **iodine**. These have **high atomic numbers**, so they show up clearly in X-ray images and can be followed as they move through a patient's body.

CAT Scans use X-rays

1) **Computerised axial tomography** (CT or CAT) scans produce an image of a **two-dimensional slice** through the body.

2) The patient lies on a table, which slides in and out of a **ring**. This ring is made up of **detectors** and a rotating **X-ray beam**.

3) The **X-ray beam fans out** and **rotates** around the body. It is picked up by the **detectors**. A computer works out how much **attenuation** has been caused by each part of the body and produces a **high quality** image.

4) CAT scans produce **more detailed** images than regular X-rays, especially for **soft tissue**. The data can also be manipulated to generate a **3D image**.

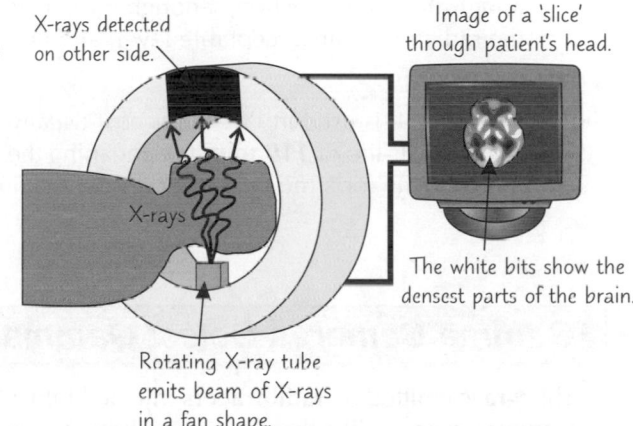

X-rays detected on other side.

Image of a 'slice' through patient's head.

X-rays

The white bits show the densest parts of the brain.

Rotating X-ray tube emits beam of X-rays in a fan shape.

Practice Questions

Q1 Draw a diagram of an X-ray tube and describe the function of the cathode, filament and target metal.

Q2 State two ways to increase the beam intensity of the electron beam in an X-ray tube.

Q3 State three mechanisms which cause X-ray attenuation.

Q4 State the reasons for using an artificial contrast medium when taking an X-ray image of a patient's digestive tract.

Q5 Draw a diagram of a CAT scanner and describe how it works. Give an advantage over using X-ray scans.

Exam Questions

Q1 X-rays hit a lead block with an intensity of 200 Wm^{-2}. Lead has a linear attenuation coefficient of 27 cm^{-1}. Calculate the intensity of the X-rays 15 mm into the lead block. [1 mark]

Q2 An X-ray tube has a tube voltage of 40 kV. The tube voltage is then changed so the wavelength of the maximum energy X-ray photons emitted by the tube is a third of its original value. Calculate the new tube voltage. [2 marks]

There's more than just the bare bones of X-ray imaging here...

X-ray images are just shadow pictures — bones absorb X-rays, stop them reaching the film and create a white 'shadow'.

Medical Uses of Nuclear Radiation

Radiation can be incredibly useful in medicine, but any use of radiation carries some risk.

Medical Tracers are Used to Diagnose the Function of Organs

1) **Medical tracers** are **radioactive substances** that are used to show tissue or **organ function**. Other types of imaging, **e.g. X-rays**, only show the **structure** of organs — medical tracers show **structure and function**.

2) **Medical tracers** usually consist of a **radioactive isotope** — e.g. **technetium-99m** or **fluorine-18** — bound to a **substance** that is **used** by the **body** — e.g. **glucose** or **water**.

3) The tracer is **injected** into or **swallowed** by the patient and then **moves** through the **body** to the region of interest. **Where** the tracer goes depends on the **substance** the isotope is bound to — i.e. it goes anywhere that the substance would **normally go**, and is used how that substance is **normally used**.

4) The **radiation emitted** is **recorded** (e.g. by a **gamma camera** or **PET scanner** — see below and next page) and an **image** of inside the patient produced.

- Tracers can show areas of **damaged tissue** in the heart by detecting areas of **decreased blood flow**. This can reveal **coronary artery disease** and damaged or dead heart muscle caused by **heart attacks**.
- They can identify **active cancer tumours** by showing **metabolic activity** in tissue. **Cancer cells** have a **much higher metabolism** than healthy cells because they're growing fast, so take up more tracer.
- Tracers can show **blood flow and activity** in the **brain**. This helps **research** and **treat** neurological conditions like Parkinson's, Alzheimer's, epilepsy, depression, etc.

Technetium-99m is widely used in medical tracers because it emits γ-**radiation**, has a **half-life of 6 hours** (long enough for data to be recorded, but short enough to limit the radiation to an acceptable level) and **decays** to a **much more stable isotope**.

Fluorine-18 is used in **PET scans** as it usually undergoes **beta plus** decay. It has a half-life of **110 minutes**, meaning the patient is exposed to radioactivity for a much **shorter** amount of time than with **technetium-99m**.

Gamma Cameras Detect Gamma Radiation

The γ-**rays** emitted by **radiotracers** injected into a patient's body are detected using a **gamma camera**. Gamma cameras (like the one shown **below**) consist of **five** main parts:

1) **Lead shield** — **stops radiation** from **other sources** entering the camera.
2) **Lead collimator** — a **piece of lead** with thousands of **vertical holes** in it — only γ-rays **parallel** to the holes can **pass through**.
3) **Sodium iodide crystal** — emits a **flash of light** (**scintillates**) whenever a γ-**ray** hits it.
4) **Photomultiplier tubes** — **detect** the flashes of **light** from the crystal and turn them into **pulses of electricity**.
5) **Electronic circuit** — **collects** the signals from the photomultiplier tubes and sends them to a **computer** for processing into an **image** which is used to help the doctor **diagnose** the patient.

Gamma cameras are useful in helping to **diagnose** patients without the need for **surgery**. They are **cheaper** than a PET scanner but are still fairly **expensive**. They also use **ionising radiation** which is bad for you — see the next page.

Medical Uses of Nuclear Radiation

PET Scanning Involves Positron/Electron Annihilation

1) In a PET (**positron emission tomography**) scan, the patient is injected with a substance used by the body, e.g. glucose, containing a **positron-emitting** radiotracer with a **short half-life**, e.g. ^{13}N, ^{15}O, ^{18}F.

2) The patient is left for a time to allow the radiotracer to **move through the body** to the organs.

3) **Positrons** emitted by the radioisotope collide with **electrons** in the organs, causing them to **annihilate**, emitting **high-energy gamma rays** in the process.

4) **Detectors** around the body record these **gamma rays**, and a computer builds up a **map of the radioactivity** in the body.

5) The **distribution of radioactivity** matches up with **metabolic activity**. This is because **more** of the radioactive glucose (or whatever) injected into the patient is taken up and **used** by cells that are **doing more work** (cells with an **increased metabolism**, in other words).

6) By looking at which **cells** are doing more **work**, doctors can help **diagnose** illnesses in patients — like detecting the **higher activity** of cancer cells, p.82. PET scanners allow patients to be diagnosed without having to have **surgery** and the **radiotracers** used have a **short half-life** so the patient is **exposed** to radiation for only a **short time**.

7) However, this short time period means there is only a **limited** time when a patient can be scanned — unlike with gamma cameras, where the tracer takes much longer to decay. PET scanners are also incredibly **expensive**, meaning not many hospitals own one. This means some doctors may have to make **difficult decisions** about whether a patient should be sent for a PET scan.

- PET scanner
- γ-rays
- positron-electron annihilation
- γ-rays detected
- map of a 'slice' through patient's head showing concentration of radiotracer

Ionising Radiation is Used When the Benefits Outweigh the Risks

X-rays, **γ-rays**, and α and β **particles** are all classed as **ionising radiation**. When they **interact** with matter they **ionise atoms** or **molecules** to form **ions** — usually by **removing an electron** — and this can **damage** cells. Cell damage is bad news — it can cause:

1) **Cell mutations** and **cancerous tumours** by altering or damaging the cell's DNA.
2) **Cell sterility** by stopping the cell from reproducing.
3) **Cell death** — the cell is destroyed completely.

The **macroscopic effects** of ionising radiation (i.e. the large-scale effects) include **tumours**, **skin burns**, **sterility**, **radiation sickness**, **hair loss** and **death** — nice. The result is that radiation is only used when the **benefits** to the patient **outweigh** the risks — i.e. **radiation** doses are **limited** and only used when it's **absolutely necessary**.

Practice Questions

Q1 Why are medical tracers useful?
Q2 What are the five main parts of a gamma camera?
Q3 Describe how an image is formed in PET scanning.
Q4 What are the drawbacks of using medical tracers?

Exam Question

Q1 A doctor suspects that his patient has a cancerous tumour. Describe a non-invasive technique that could be used to confirm the doctor's diagnosis, giving one advantage and one disadvantage of this method. [4 marks]

The biological effects of a page on radiation — a sore head...
The radiation emitted by medical tracers is used to help diagnose patients without sending them for exploratory surgery.

Ultrasound Imaging

Ultrasound is a 'sound' with higher frequencies than we can hear.

Ultrasound has a Higher Frequency than Humans can Hear

1) Ultrasound waves are **longitudinal** waves with **higher frequencies** than humans can hear (>20 000 Hz).

2) For **medical** purposes, frequencies are usually from **1** to **15 MHz**.

3) When an ultrasound wave meets a **boundary** between two **different materials**, some of it is **reflected** and some of it passes through (undergoing **refraction** if the **angle of incidence** is **not 90°**).

4) The **reflected waves** are detected by the **ultrasound scanner** and are used to **generate an image**.

The Amount of Reflection depends on the Change in Acoustic Impedance

1) The **acoustic impedance**, **Z**, of a medium is defined as: $$Z = \rho c$$ where ρ is the density of the material and c is the speed of sound in that material
    Z has units of $kgm^{-2}s^{-1}$.

2) Say an ultrasound wave travels through a material with an impedance Z_1. It hits the boundary between this material and another with an impedance Z_2. The incident wave has an intensity of I_0.

3) If the two materials have a **large difference** in **impedance**, then **most** of the energy is **reflected** (the intensity of the reflected wave I_r will be high). If the impedance of the two materials is the **same** then there is **no reflection**.

4) The **fraction** of wave **intensity** that is reflected is given by: $$\frac{I_r}{I_0} = \frac{(Z_2 - Z_1)^2}{(Z_2 + Z_1)^2}$$

    You don't need to learn this equation. Just practise using it.

There are Advantages and Disadvantages to Ultrasound Imaging

ADVANTAGES:

1) There are **no** known **hazards** — in particular, **no** exposure to **ionising radiation**.

2) It's good for imaging **soft tissues**, since you can obtain **real-time** images.

3) Ultrasound devices are relatively **cheap** and **portable**.

4) The scan is a **quick procedure** (10-15 minutes) and the patient **can move** during the scan.

DISADVANTAGES:

1) Ultrasound **doesn't penetrate bone** — so it **can't** be used to **detect fractures** or examine the **brain**.

2) Ultrasound **cannot** pass through **air spaces** in the body (due to the **mismatch** in **impedance**) — so it can't produce images from behind the lungs.

3) It **can't** give detail on **solid masses**.

4) Ultrasound **can't** give information about any **solid masses found**.

Ultrasound Images are Produced Using the Piezoelectric Effect

1) **Piezoelectric crystals** produce a **potential difference** when they are **deformed** (squashed or stretched) — the rearrangement in structure displaces the **centres of symmetry** of their electric **charges**.

2) When you **apply a p.d.** across a piezoelectric crystal, the crystal **deforms**. If the p.d. is **alternating**, then the crystal **vibrates** at the **same frequency**.

3) A piezoelectric crystal can act as a **receiver** of **ultrasound**, converting **sound waves** into **alternating voltages**, and also as a **transmitter**, converting **alternating voltages** into **sound waves**.

4) Ultrasound transducers use **lead zirconate titanate (PZT)** crystals. The **thickness** of the crystal is **half the wavelength** of the ultrasound that it produces. Ultrasound of this frequency will make the crystal **resonate** (see p.20) and produce a large signal.

5) The PZT crystal is **heavily damped**, to produce **short pulses** and **increase** the **resolution** of the device.

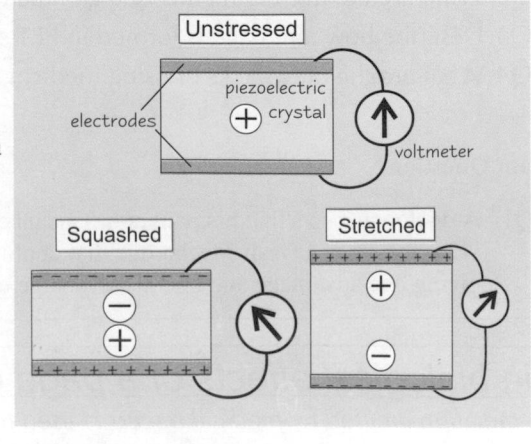

Ultrasound Imaging

You need a *Coupling Medium* between the *Transducer* and the *Body*

1) **Soft tissue** has a very different **acoustic impedance** from **air**, so almost all the ultrasound **energy** is **reflected** from the surface of the body if there is air between the **transducer** and the **body**.

2) To avoid this, you need a **coupling medium** (usually a **gel**) between the transducer and the body — this **displaces** the **air** and has an impedance much closer to that of body tissue. The use of **coupling media** is an example of **impedance matching**.

The *A-Scan* is a *Range Measuring* System

1) The **amplitude scan** (**A-Scan**) sends a short **pulse** of ultrasound into the body simultaneously with an **electron beam** sweeping across a cathode ray oscilloscope (**CRO**) screen.

2) The scanner receives **reflected** ultrasound pulses that appear as **vertical deflections** on the CRO screen. Weaker pulses (that have travelled further in the body and **arrive later**) are **amplified** more to avoid the loss of valuable data — this process is called **time-gain compensation** (**TGC**).

3) The **horizontal positions** of the reflected pulses indicate the **time** the 'echo' took to return, and are used to work out **distances** between structures in the body (e.g. the **diameter** of a **baby's head** in the uterus).

4) A **stream** of pulses can produce a **steady image** on the screen, although modern CROs can store a digital image after just one exposure.

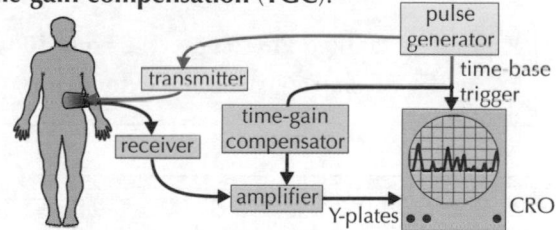

In a *B-Scan*, the *Brightness* Varies

1) In a **brightness scan** (**B-Scan**), the electron beam sweeps **down** the screen rather than across.

2) The amplitude of the reflected pulses is displayed as the **brightness** of the spot.

3) You can use a **linear array** of transducers to produce a **two-dimensional** image.

Ultrasound Waves are Affected by the *Doppler Effect*

1) Ultrasound waves reflected at an angle to **moving** cells undergo a change of **frequency** (or wavelength). This is caused by the **Doppler effect** (p.36).

2) This change of frequency (beat frequency) can allow doctors to find the **speed** at which those cells are moving (for example, blood cells in an artery).

$$\frac{\Delta f}{f} = \frac{2v\cos\theta}{c} \quad \text{or} \quad v = \frac{c\Delta f}{2f\cos\theta}$$

where f is initial frequency, Δf is change in frequency, v is the velocity of the moving cell, c is the speed of sound in that medium and θ is the angle between the ultrasound receiver and the direction in which the cell is moving.

Practice Questions

Q1 What is ultrasound? How are ultrasound waves produced and received in an ultrasound transducer?

Q2 What are the two types of ultrasound scan? Give one use of ultrasound scans.

Q3 Explain how ultrasound imaging can be used to detect the speed of blood in an artery.

Exam Questions

Q1 The acoustic impedance of a certain soft tissue is 1.63×10^6 kgm^{-2}s^{-1} and its density is 1.09×10^3 kgm^{-3}. Calculate the velocity at which the ultrasound waves travel in this medium. [2 marks]

Q2 Calculate the ratio between the intensity of the ultrasound that enters the body when a coupling gel is used and when none is used (and there is an air gap). Give your answer to the nearest power of ten. ($Z_{gel} = 1500 \times 10^3$ kgm^{-2}s^{-1}, $Z_{air} = 0.430 \times 10^3$ kgm^{-2}s^{-1}, $Z_{tissue} = 1630 \times 10^3$ kgm^{-2}s^{-1}) [5 marks]

Ultrasound — Mancunian for 'très bien'

You can use ultrasound to make images in cases where X-rays would do too much damage — like to check up on the development of a baby in the womb. You have to know what you're looking for though, or it just looks like a blob.

Exam Structure and Technique

Good exam technique can make a big difference to your mark, so make sure you read this stuff carefully.

Get Familiar With the **Exam Structure**

For A-level Physics, you'll be sitting **three papers**. Find out your **exam timetable** and use the info below to **plan** your revision carefully.

You'll also do a Practical Endorsement as part of your A-level. It'll involve doing practicals throughout the course, and will be reported separately from your exam results.

Paper 1 — Modelling Physics **2 hours 15 minutes** **37%** of your A-level **100 marks: 15** for **Section A** (**multiple choice** questions) **85** for **Section B** (**short answer** and **extended response** questions)	Covers material from **modules 1, 2 and 3** (from year 1 of A-level) **and** **module 5** of this book.
Paper 2 — Exploring Physics **2 hours 15 minutes** **37%** of your A-level **100 marks: 15** for **Section A** (**multiple choice** questions) **85** for **Section B** (**short answer** and **extended response** questions)	Covers material from **modules 1, 2 and 4** (from year 1 of A-level) **and** **module 6** of this book.
Paper 3 — Unified Physics **1 hour 30 minutes** **26%** of your A-level **70 marks:** all **short answer** and **extended response** questions.	Covers material from **all modules (1-6)** from years 1 and 2 of A-level.

Make Sure You **Read the Question**

1) It sounds obvious, but it's really important you read each question **carefully**, and give an answer that matches what you've been asked.

2) Look for **command words** in the question — they'll give you an idea of the **kind of answer** you should write. Commonly used command words for written questions are **state**, **describe**, **discuss** and **explain**:

- If a question asks you to **state** something, you just need to give a **definition**, **example** or **fact**.
- If you're asked to **describe** what happens in a particular situation, don't waste time explaining why it happens — that's not what the question is after.
- For **discuss** questions, you'll need to include more **detail** — depending on the question you might need to cover what happens, what the effects are, and perhaps include a brief explanation of why it happens.
- If a question asks you to **explain** why something happens you must give **reasons**, not just a description.

3) Look at **how many marks** a question is worth before answering. It'll tell you roughly **how much information** you need to include. See the next page for more about **wordy questions**.

Manage Your **Time** Sensibly

1) The **number of marks** tells you roughly **how long** to spend on a question — you've got just over a minute per mark in the exam. If you get stuck on a question for too long, it may be best to **move on** so you don't run out of time for the others.

2) The **multiple choice questions** are only worth **one mark each**, so it's not worth stressing over one for ages if you get stuck — **move on** and come back to it later.

3) You don't have to work through the paper **in order** — you could leave questions on topics you find harder until last.

Giles didn't like to brag, but his time-management skills were excellent.

Don't be **Put Off** if a Question Seems **Strange**

1) You may get some weird questions that seem to have nothing to do with anything you've learnt. **DON'T PANIC.** Every question will be something you can answer **using physics you know**, it just may be in a new **context**.

2) Answering these **trickier questions** will get you **top marks**, but make sure you get the **easier marks** in the bag first.

3) All of the A-level exams could **pull together** ideas from different parts of physics, so check the question for any **keywords** that you recognise. For example, if a question talks about acceleration, think about the rules and equations you know, and whether any of them apply to the situation in the question.

Exam Structure and Technique

Watch out for *Practical Questions...*

1) You covered modules 1 and 2 in year 1 of A-level and each paper could test anything in module 1 (on practical skills) or on **uncertainty** in module 2. You may have to **describe an experiment** to investigate something, or **answer questions** on an experiment you've been given.

2) These could be experiments you've **met before**, or they could be **entirely new** to you. All the questions will be based on physics that you've **covered**, but may include bits from different topics put together in ways you haven't seen before. Don't let this put you off, just **think carefully** about what's going on.

3) Make sure you know the difference between **precision**, **accuracy** and **validity** (from module 1). Learn what **uncertainty**, **random errors** and **systematic errors** are (from module 2) and make sure you can give some examples of where each might come from.

4) You need to be able to **calculate errors** and **plot** and **interpret graphs** too.

...and Wordy Ones

For some questions, you'll need to write a slightly longer answer, where the '**quality** of your **extended response**' will be taken into account. You'll need to make sure you can develop a **clear** and **logical**, **well-structured line of reasoning**, backed up with **relevant information**.

You can avoid losing marks in these questions by making sure you do the following things:

1) Think about your answer before you write it. Your answer needs to be **logically structured** to get the top marks.

2) Make sure your answer is **relevant** to the question being asked and that you **explain** your ideas or argument **clearly**. It's dead easy to go off on a tangent.

3) Back up your points with **evidence** or **explanation**. You'll lose marks if you just make statements without supporting them.

4) Write in **whole sentences** and keep an eye on your **spelling**, **grammar** and **punctuation**. It'll help make sure your answer is clear and easy to read.

Questions like this will be marked in some way in the exam — e.g. with an asterisk (*). Check the instructions on the front of your paper to find out.

Example: A large group of people walk across a footbridge. When the frequency of the group's footsteps is 1 Hz, the bridge noticeably oscillates.

Describe the phenomenon causing the bridge to oscillate, and suggest what engineers could do to solve this problem.   *[6 marks]*

Good Answer

The pedestrians provide a driving force on the bridge, causing it to oscillate. At around 1 Hz, the driving frequency from the pedestrians is roughly equal to the natural frequency of the bridge, causing it to resonate. The amplitude of the bridge's oscillations when resonating at 1 Hz will be greater than at any other driving frequency. The oscillations at this frequency are large enough to be noticed by pedestrians. Engineers could fix this problem by critically damping the bridge to stop any oscillations as quickly as possible. They could also adjust the natural frequency of the bridge so that it was not so close to a known walking frequency of large groups of people.

Bad Answer

resonance
driving frequency = natural frequency
damping

There's nothing fundamentally wrong with the physics in the bad answer, but you'd miss out on some nice easy marks just for not bothering to link the physics with the context given and not putting your answer into proper sentences.

The penultimate joke in the book better be good... here goes... Oh, I've run out of space...

Making sure you're prepared for what the exams will be like, reading questions carefully and managing your time all sounds like pretty basic advice, but you'd be surprised how many people don't follow it. Make sure you do...

Maths Skills

At least 40% of the marks up for grabs in A-level Physics will require maths skills, so make sure you know your stuff. As well as being given some tricky calculations, you could be asked to work with exponentials and logarithms and work out values from log graphs. And it's easy when you know how...

Be Careful With Calculations

1) In calculation questions you should always **show your working** —
you may get some marks for your **method** even if you get the answer wrong.

2) Don't **round** your answer until the **very end**. A lot of calculations in A-level Physics are
quite **long**, and if you round too early you could introduce errors to your final answer.

3) Be careful with **units**. Lots of formulas require quantities to be in specific units (e.g. time in seconds), so
it's best to **convert** any numbers you're given into these before you start. And obviously, if the question
tells you which units to give your **answer** in, don't throw away marks by giving it in different ones.

4) You should give your final answer to the same number of **significant figures** as the data that you use from
the question with the **least number** of significant figures (or one more). If you can, write out the **unrounded**
answer, then your **rounded** answer with the number of significant figures you've given it to — it shows you
know your stuff.

Many Relationships in Physics are Exponential

A fair few of the relationships you need to know about in A-level Physics are **exponential** — where the **rate
of change** of a quantity is **proportional** to the **amount** of the quantity left. Here are a few that crop up in the
A-level course (if they don't ring a bell, go have a quick read about them)...

Charge on a capacitor — the decay of charge on a discharging
capacitor is proportional to the amount of charge left on the capacitor:
$$Q = Q_0 e^{\frac{-t}{CR}}$$ (see p.44)

    There are also exponential relationships for I and V and for charging capacitors.

Radioactive decay — the rate of decay of a radioactive sample is
proportional to the **number of undecayed nuclei** in the sample:
$$N = N_0 e^{-\lambda t}$$ (see p.75)

The activity of a radioactive sample behaves in the same way.

X-ray attenuation — the reduction of **intensity** of X-rays
over distance is proportional to their **initial intensity**:
$$I = I_0 e^{-\mu x}$$ (see p.81)

You can Plot Exponential Relations Using the Natural Log, ln

1) Say you've got two variables, x and y, which are related to each other
by the formula $y = ke^{-ax}$ (where k and a are constants).

2) The **natural logarithm** of x, **ln x**, is the power
to which e (the base) must be raised to to give x.

    *A logarithm can be to any base you want. Another common
one is 'base 10' which is usually written as 'log$_{10}$' or just 'log'.*

3) So, by definition, $e^{\ln x} = x$ and $\ln(e^x) = x$.
So far so good... now you need some **log rules**:

$$\ln(AB) = \ln A + \ln B \qquad \ln\left(\frac{A}{B}\right) = \ln A - \ln B \qquad \ln x^n = n \ln x$$

*These log rules work for all logs
(including the natural logarithm) and
you're given them on your formula sheet.*

4) So, for $y = ke^{-ax}$, if you take the natural log of both sides of the equation you get:

$$\ln y = \ln(ke^{-ax}) = \ln k + \ln(e^{-ax}) \implies \boxed{\ln y = \ln k - ax}$$

5) Then all you need to do is plot ($\ln y$) against x, and Eric's your aunty: $\implies$

You get a **straight-line graph** with (**ln k**) as
the **vertical intercept**, and **–a** as the **gradient**.

Maths Skills

You Might be Asked to find the **Gradient** of a Log Graph

This log business isn't too bad when you get your head around which bit of the log graph means what.

Example: The graph shows the radioactive decay of isotope X.

a) Find the initial number of undecayed nuclei, N_0, in the sample.

You know that the number of undecayed nuclei in a sample, N, is related to the initial number of undecayed nuclei, N_0, by the equation $N = N_0 e^{-\lambda t}$.

So: $\ln N = \ln N_0 - \lambda t$

The y-intercept of the graph is $\ln N_0 = 9.2$

$N_0 = e^{9.2} = 9897.129... =$ **9900 nuclei (to 2 s.f.)**

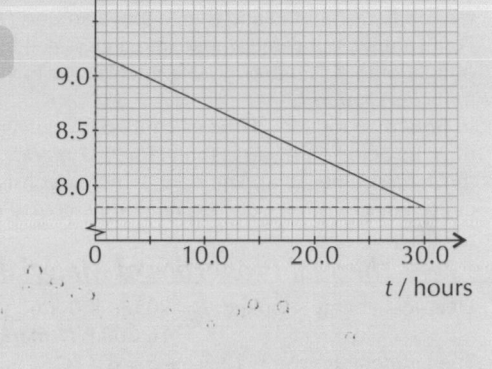

b) Find the decay constant λ of isotope X.

$-\lambda$ is the gradient of the graph, so: $\lambda = \dfrac{\Delta \ln N}{\Delta t} = \dfrac{9.2 - 7.8}{30.0 \times 60 \times 60} =$ **1.3×10^{-5} s^{-1} (to 2 s.f.)**

You can Plot **Any Power Law** as a **Log-Log Graph**

You can use logs to plot a straight-line graph of **any power law** — it doesn't have to be an exponential.

Say the relationship between two variables x and y is:

$$y = kx^n$$

Take the **log** (base 10) of both sides to get:

$$\log y = \log k + n \log x$$

When it came to logs, Geoff always took time to smell the flowers...

So **$\log k$** will be the **y-intercept** and **n** will be the **gradient** of the graph.

Example: A physicist carries out an experiment to determine the nuclear radius R (in m) of various elements, which have nucleon number A. She plots a line of best fit for her results on a graph of $\log R$ against $\log A$. Part of the graph is shown. Using the equation $R = r_0 A^{1/3}$, find the value of the constant r_0 from the graph.

First take logs of both sides:

$\log R = \log (r_0 A^{1/3}) = \log r_0 + \log A^{1/3}$
$\qquad\qquad\qquad\quad = \log r_0 + \dfrac{1}{3} \log A$

> Look back at page 62 for more on nuclear radius.

Comparing this to the equation of a straight line (in the form $y = mx + c$), you can see that the gradient of the graph is $\dfrac{1}{3}$ and the vertical intercept is $\log r_0$.

So, reading from the graph, the vertical intercept is about -14.9.

$\log r_0 = -14.9$, so $r_0 = 10^{-14.9} = 1.258... \times 10^{-15} =$ **1.3 fm (to 2 s.f.)**

> If $a = \log_{10} b$, then $b = 10^a$.

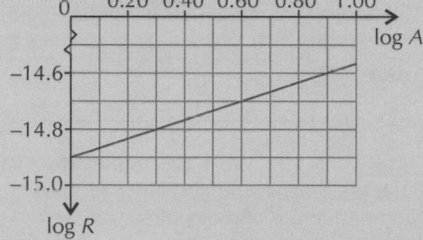

Lumberjacks are great musicians — they have a natural logarhythm...

Well, that's it folks. Crack open the chocolate bar of victory and know you've earned it. Only the tiny detail of the actual exam to go... ahem. Make sure you know which bit means what on a log graph and you'll pick up some nice easy marks. Other than that, stay calm, be as clear as you can and good luck — I've got my fingers, toes and eyes crossed for you.

Answers

Module 5: Section 1 — Thermal Physics

Page 5 — Phases of Matter and Temperature

1 In a solid the particles are very close together in a lattice structure and vibrate a little *[1 mark]*. In a liquid the particles are still quite close together but are free to move past each other *[1 mark]*. In a gas the particles are far apart, are randomly distributed and free to move around *[1 mark]*.

2 a) For example, put some smoke into a glass cell and shine a beam of light onto it *[1 mark]*. Use a microscope to view the smoke particles *[1 mark]*.

   b) In Brownian motion, particles continually change direction so must be acted on by an external force *[1 mark]*. The nature of this force is uneven and random, which is consistent with a force caused by collisions between randomly moving particles *[1 mark]*.

Page 7 — Thermal Properties of Materials

1 Electrical energy supplied: $E = 90.0 \times 3.0 \times 60$
$= 16\ 200$ J *[1 mark]*
The temperature rise is $12.7 - 4.5 = 8.2\ °C$

$E = mc\Delta\theta$, so $c = \dfrac{E}{m\Delta\theta}$

so $c = \dfrac{16\ 200}{2.0 \times 8.2} = 987.8... = $ **990 Jkg^{-1}°C^{-1} (to 2 s.f.)**

[1 mark for correct number, 1 mark for correct unit.]
You need the right unit for the third mark — Jkg^{-1}K^{-1} would be right too.

2 The heat transferred to the water is equal to the heat leaving the block so: $m_w c_w (T_s - T_w) = m_b c_b (T_b - T_s)$.
Rearranging for c_b gives: $c_b = \dfrac{m_w c_w (T_s - T_w)}{m_b (T_b - T_s)}$
$c_b = \dfrac{2.0 \times 4180 \times (26 - 19)}{4.0(100 - 26)}$ *[1 mark]*
$= 197.7... = $ **200 J kg^{-1} K^{-1} (to 2 s.f.)** *[1 mark]*

3 Total amount of energy needed to boil all the water:
$E = mL = 0.500 \times 2.26 \times 10^6 = 1.13 \times 10^6$ J *[1 mark]*
3.00 kW means you get 3000 J in a second, so
time in seconds $= 1.13 \times 10^6 \div 3000$ *[1 mark]*
$= 376.6... = $ **377 s (to 3 s.f.)** *[1 mark]*

Page 9 — Ideal Gases

1 $\dfrac{p}{T} = $ constant, so $\dfrac{p_1}{T_1} = \dfrac{1.04 \times 10^6}{10.0 + 273} = 3674.91...$ *[1 mark]*
$\dfrac{p_2}{T_2} = 3674.91...$ so $p_2 = 3674.91... \times (62.3 + 273)$
$= 1.232... \times 10^6$
$= $ **1.23 × 10^6 Pa (to 3 s.f.)** *[1 mark]*

2 a) i) Number of moles $= \dfrac{\text{mass of gass}}{\text{molar mass}}$
$= \dfrac{0.0140}{0.0280} = $ **0.500 moles** *[1 mark]*
   ii) Number of molecules = number of moles × Avogadro's
constant $= 0.500 \times 6.02 \times 10^{23} = $ **3.01 × 10^{23}** *[1 mark]*

   b) $pV = nRT$, so $p = \dfrac{nRT}{V}$
$p = \dfrac{0.5 \times 8.31 \times (27.0 + 273)}{0.0100}$ *[1 mark]*
$= 124\ 650 = $ **125 000 Pa (to 3 s.f.)** *[1 mark]*

   c) The pressure would also halve *[1 mark]* (because it is proportional to the number of molecules — $pV = NkT$).

3 $\dfrac{pV}{T} = $ constant
At ground level, $\dfrac{pV}{T} = \dfrac{1.00 \times 10^5 \times 10.0}{293}$
$= 3412.9...$ JK^{-1} *[1 mark]*
Higher up, $\dfrac{pV}{T}$ will equal this same constant.
So higher up, $p = \dfrac{\text{constant} \times T}{V} = \dfrac{3412.9... \times 261}{25.0}$ *[1 mark]*
$= 35\ 631.39... = $ **35 600 Pa (to 3 s.f.)** *[1 mark]*

Page 11 — The Pressure of an Ideal Gas

1 Pressure is affected by the volume of the container — increasing the volume lowers the frequency of collisions between particles and the container walls, so pressure decreases *[1 mark]*. The number of particles also affects pressure — more particles means the frequency of collisions between particles and the container will increase, increasing the total force exerted by all the collisions *[1 mark]*. Because force is proportional to mass ($F = ma$), heavier particles will also increase the total force exerted on the container by collisions, increasing the pressure *[1 mark]*. The speed of particles also affects the change in momentum when particles collide with the container, changing the force exerted on the container and therefore the pressure *[1 mark]*.

2 a) $pV = \frac{1}{3}Nm\overline{c^2}$ Rearrange the equation: $\overline{c^2} = \dfrac{3pV}{Nm}$
$\overline{c^2} = \dfrac{3 \times (1.03 \times 10^5) \times (7.00 \times 10^{-5})}{(2.17 \times 10^{22}) \times (6.65 \times 10^{-27})}$ *[1 mark]*
$= 149\ 890.8... = $ **150 000 m^{2}s^{-2} (to 3 s.f.)** *[1 mark]*

   b) r.m.s. speed $= \sqrt{\overline{c^2}} = \sqrt{149\ 890.8...} = 387.15...$
$= $ **387 ms^{-1} (to 3 s.f.)** *[1 mark]*

Page 13 — Internal Energy of an Ideal Gas

1 a) 6.02×10^{23} molecules *[1 mark]*
   b) $E = \frac{3}{2}kT = \frac{3}{2} \times (1.38 \times 10^{-23}) \times 300$ *[1 mark]*
$= $ **6.21 × 10^{-21} J** *[1 mark]*
   c) The nitrogen molecules are constantly colliding and transferring energy between themselves, so have different energies *[1 mark]*.

2 a) $U = \frac{3}{2}NkT$ so $\Delta U = \frac{3}{2}Nk\Delta T$
$\Delta U = \frac{3}{2} \times 3.00 \times 10^{23} \times 1.38 \times 10^{-23} \times (500 - 300)$ *[1 mark]*
$= 1242 = $ **1240 J (to 3 s.f.)** *[1 mark]*
   b) $pV = NkT$ so $V = \dfrac{NkT}{p}$
$V = \dfrac{3.00 \times 10^{23} \times 1.38 \times 10^{-23} \times 500}{1.66 \times 10^4}$ *[1 mark]*
$= 0.1246... = $ **0.125 m^3 (to 3 s.f.)** *[1 mark]*

Module 5: Section 2 — Circular Motion and Oscillations

Page 15 — Circular Motion

1 a) $\omega = \theta/t = 2\pi / 3.2 \times 10^7 = 1.963... \times 10^{-7}$
$= $ **2.0 × 10^{-7} rad s^{-1} (to 2 s.f.)** *[1 mark]*
$v = r\omega = 1.5 \times 10^{11} \times 1.963... \times 10^{-7} = 29452.43...$ms^{-1}
$= $ **30 kms^{-1} (to 2 s.f.)** *[1 mark]*
   b) $F = m\omega^2 r = 6.0 \times 10^{24} \times (1.963... \times 10^{-7})^2 \times 1.5 \times 10^{11}$
$= 3.469... \times 10^{22} = $ **3.5 × 10^{22} N (to 2 s.f.)** *[1 mark]*
This is the gravitational force between the Sun and Earth *[1 mark]*.

2 a) To stop the water from falling out of the bucket at the top of its swing, the acceleration due to gravity must be equal to or less than the acceleration due to the bucket's circular motion, so $\omega^2 r \geq g$ *[1 mark]*.
f is at a minimum when ω is at a minimum, so find the smallest value of ω for which $\omega^2 r \geq g$:
$\omega^2 r = g$ where $r = 1$ m and $g = 9.81$ ms^{-2}, so $\omega^2 = 9.81$
$\omega = 3.132...$ rads^{-1} *[1 mark]*
$\omega = 2\pi f$ so $f = \omega/2\pi = 3.132... \div 2\pi = 0.498...$
$= $ **0.5 Hz (to 1 s.f.)** *[1 mark]*
   b) $F = m\omega^2 r = 10 \times 5^2 \times 1 = 250$ N *[1 mark]*
This force is provided by both the tension in the rope, T, and gravity: $T + (10 \times 9.81) = 250$.
So $T = 250 - (10 \times 9.81) = 151.9 = $ **150 N (to 2 s.f.)** *[1 mark]*

Page 17 — Simple Harmonic Motion

1 a) Simple harmonic motion is an oscillation in which the acceleration of an object is directly proportional to its displacement from the midpoint *[1 mark]*, and is directed towards the midpoint *[1 mark]*.

b) The acceleration of a falling bouncy ball is constant, so the motion is not SHM. *[1 mark]*.

2 a) Maximum velocity $= \omega A = (2\pi f)A = 2\pi \times 1.5 \times 0.05 = 0.4712...$
$= \textbf{0.47 ms}^{-1}$ **(to 2 s.f.)** *[1 mark]*

b) $x = A\cos(\omega t) = A\cos(2\pi ft) = 0.05 \times \cos(2\pi \times 1.5 \times 0.1)$
$= 0.0294... = \textbf{0.029 m}$ **(to 2 s.f.)** *[1 mark]*

c) $x = A\cos(\omega t) = A\cos(2\pi ft)$ so $0.01 = 0.05 \times \cos(2\pi \times 1.5t)$
$0.01 \div 0.05 = \cos(2\pi \times 1.5t)$
$0.2 = \cos(3\pi t)$ so $\cos^{-1}(0.2) = 3\pi t$ *[1 mark]*
$3\pi t = 1.369...$ so $t = 0.145... = \textbf{0.15 s}$ **(to 2 s.f.)** *[1 mark]*
Don't forget to put your calculator in radian mode when you're solving questions on circular motion — it's an easy mistake to make.

3 $\omega_X = 2\omega_Y$ and maximum acceleration $= \omega^2 A$
$a_{max, X} = \omega_X^2 A = (2\omega_Y)^2 A = 4\omega_Y^2 A$
$a_{max, Y} = \omega_Y^2 A$, so $a_{max, X} = 4a_{max, Y}$
D *[1 mark]*

Page 19 — Investigating Simple Harmonic Motion

1 a) E.g. hang a mass from the spring. Suspend the spring (from a length of string) above a position sensor attached to a data logger *[1 mark]* then lift the mass slightly and let it go to start the mass oscillating *[1 mark]*. Measure the time period of the oscillation from the displacement-time graph generated by the computer *[1 mark]*. Repeat the experiment for different masses, then plot time period against mass *[1 mark]*.

b) The time period increases with increasing mass *[1 mark]* and the relationship is not linear *[1 mark]*.

Page 21 — Free and Forced Vibrations

1 a) When a system is forced to vibrate at a frequency that's close to, or the same as, its natural frequency *[1 mark]* and oscillates with a much larger than usual amplitude *[1 mark]*.

b) E.g.

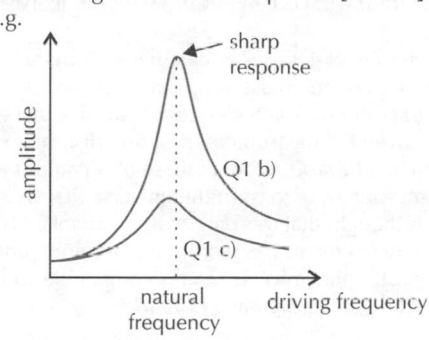

[1 mark for showing a peak at the natural frequency, 1 mark for a sharp peak.]

c) *[See graph in part b). 1 mark for a smaller peak at the natural frequency.]*
The peak will actually be slightly to the left of the natural frequency due to the damping, but you'll get the mark if the peak is at the same frequency in the diagram.

2 A system is critically damped if it returns to rest in the shortest time possible when it's displaced from equilibrium and released *[1 mark]*. It is used in e.g. the suspension in a car *[1 mark]*.

Module 5: Section 3 — Gravitational Fields

Page 23 — Gravitational Fields

1 $g = -\dfrac{GM}{r^2}$ so $M = -\dfrac{gr^2}{G}$

$M = -\dfrac{-9.81 \times (6400 \times 10^3)^2}{6.67 \times 10^{-11}}$ *[1 mark]*

$= 6.024... \times 10^{24} = \textbf{6.0} \times \textbf{10}^{24}$ **kg (to 2 s.f.)** *[1 mark]*

2 a) $g = -\dfrac{GM}{r^2} = -\dfrac{6.67 \times 10^{-11} \times 7.35 \times 10^{22}}{(1740 \times 10^3)^2}$

$= -1.619... = \textbf{-1.6 Nkg}^{-1}$ **(to 2 s.f.)** *[1 mark]*

b) $F = -\dfrac{GMm}{r^2} = -\dfrac{6.67 \times 10^{-11} \times 7.35 \times 10^{22} \times 25}{((1740 \times 10^3) + 10)^2}$ *[1 mark]*

$= -40.4... = \textbf{-40 N}$ **(to 2 s.f.)** *[1 mark]*

3 $\dfrac{-GM}{r_1^2} = 4$ and $\dfrac{-GM}{r_2^2} = 2$ so $4r_1^2 = 2r_2^2$
so $r_2 = \sqrt{2}\,r_1$
If g decreases until it's at half of its original value, r will increase by a factor of $\sqrt{2} \sim 1.4$. So the answer is **B** *[1 mark]*

Page 25 — Gravitational Potential and Energy

1 a) At the surface: $V_g = \dfrac{-GM}{r}$ so $r = \dfrac{-GM}{V_g}$

$r = \dfrac{-6.67 \times 10^{-11} \times 2.67 \times 10^{19}}{-1.52 \times 10^4}$ *[1 mark]*

$= 117163.8... = \textbf{117 000 m}$ **(to 3 s.f.)** *[1 mark]*

b) $v = \sqrt{\dfrac{2GM}{r}} = \sqrt{\dfrac{2 \times 6.67 \times 10^{-11} \times 2.67 \times 10^{19}}{117163.8...}}$

$v = 174.3...... = \textbf{174 ms}^{-1}$ **(to 3 s.f.)** *[1 mark]*

c) V_g at 2000 m above the surface $= \dfrac{-GM}{r}$

$= \dfrac{-6.67 \times 10^{-11} \times 2.67 \times 10^{19}}{(117163.8... + 2000)}$

$= -1.49448... \times 10^4$ *[1 mark]*

$\Delta W = m\Delta V_g$
so $\Delta W = 300 \times (-1.49448... \times 10^4 - (-1.52 \times 10^4))$ *[1 mark]*
$= 7.653... \times 10^4 = \textbf{7.65} \times \textbf{10}^4$ **J (to 3 s.f.)** *[1 mark]*

Page 27 — Motion of Masses in Gravitational Fields

1 a) $T = \sqrt{\dfrac{4\pi^2 r^3}{GM}} = \sqrt{\dfrac{4\pi^2((6400 + 200.0) \times 10^3)^3}{6.67 \times 10^{-11} \times 5.98 \times 10^{24}}}$ *[1 mark]*

$= 5334.3... \text{ s} = \textbf{5300 s or 1.5 hr}$ **(to 2 s.f.)** *[1 mark]*

b) $v = \sqrt{\dfrac{GM}{r}} = \sqrt{\dfrac{6.67 \times 10^{-11} \times 5.98 \times 10^{24}}{(6400 + 200.0) \times 10^3}}$

$= 7773.9... \text{ ms}^{-1} = \textbf{7800 ms}^{-1}$ **(to 2 s.f.)** *[1 mark]*

2 Period $= 24$ hours $= 24 \times 60 \times 60 = 86\,400$ s *[1 mark]*

Rearrange $T^2 = \dfrac{4\pi^2 r^3}{GM}$ for r

$r = \sqrt[3]{\dfrac{T^2 GM}{4\pi^2}} = \sqrt[3]{\dfrac{86400^2 \times 6.67 \times 10^{-11} \times 5.98 \times 10^{24}}{4\pi^2}}$

$r = 4.22... \times 10^7$ m *[1 mark]*
Height above Earth $= 4.22... \times 10^7 - 6.4 \times 10^6 = 35\,850\,500$ m
$= \textbf{36 000 000 m or 3.6} \times \textbf{10}^4$ **km (to 2 s.f.)** *[1 mark]*

3 50 000 years is $50\,000 \times 365 \times 24 \times 3600 = 1.57... \times 10^{12}$ s
This means the sun will have lost:
$1.57... \times 10^{12} \times 6 \times 10^9 = 9.46... \times 10^{21}$ kg of mass *[1 mark]*.
This is less than 5×10^{-7}% of the Sun's mass, so will not have caused any significant change in the Earth's orbit *[1 mark]*.

Module 5: Section 4 — Astrophysics & Cosmology

Page 29 — The Solar System & Astronomical Distances

1 Planets have almost circular orbits whereas comets have highly elliptical orbits *[1 mark]*. Comets can take millions of years to orbit the Sun; planets have much shorter periods *[1 mark]*.

2 a) A light-year is the distance travelled by a photon of light / a light wave through a vacuum in one year *[1 mark]*.

b) Light travels at a finite speed, so it takes time for light from objects to reach us *[1 mark]*. Therefore, when we look at distant objects, we are seeing them as they were in the past, when the light left them, rather than as they are now *[1 mark]*.

3 a) $(5 \times 10^{-5})° \times 3600 = 0.18$ arcseconds *[1 mark]*
$d = 1 \div 0.18 = 5.555555..... = \textbf{5.6 parsecs}$ **(to 2 s.f.)** *[1 mark]*

b) $5.55555... \times 3.1 \times 10^{16} = 1.722... \times 10^{17}$ m *[1 mark]*
$1.722... \times 10^{17} \div 9.5 \times 10^{15} = 18.12... = \textbf{18 ly}$ **(to 2 s.f.)** *[1 mark]*

Answers

Page 32 — Stellar Evolution

1 a) The Chandrasekhar limit is the maximum mass at which the electron degeneracy pressure is sufficient to counteract the force of gravity once a star has run out of fuel *[1 mark]*.

b) *5-6 marks:*
The answer clearly describes both the similarities and differences between the life cycles of high and low mass stars, and explains some of these with reference to gravity and electron degeneracy pressure. The answer has a clear, logical structure.
3-4 marks:
The answer describes the similarities and differences between the life cycles of high and low mass stars. The answer includes some explanation of why high and low mass stars evolve differently, but the answer is incomplete. The answer has some logical structure.
1-2 marks:
The answer includes a limited description of the similarities and differences between high and low mass stars, but is lacking explanation. The answer is basic and poorly structured.
0 marks:
No relevant information is given.
Here are some points your answer may include:
- Both low and high mass stars exist as main sequence stars for most of their lives.
- High mass stars spend less time as main sequence stars than low mass stars, as they use up their fuel more quickly.
- During the main sequence, both low and high mass stars fuse hydrogen in their core.
- When both low mass and high mass stars run out of hydrogen in their cores, the core contracts and the outer layers expand. The star continues to fuse hydrogen in its shells, then begins to burn helium when it becomes hot and dense enough.
- Low mass stars become red giants when they start burning hydrogen in their shells. High mass stars are able to fuse heavier nuclei than helium in their shells (up to iron) to become super red giants (rather than red giants).
- Once high and low mass stars have run out of fuel, they both start to contract.
- A low mass star contracts until its electron degeneracy pressure is enough to counteract the gravitational force, preventing the star from collapsing any further, and the star becomes stable. However, for a high mass star, the electron degeneracy pressure is not enough to counteract the contraction caused by gravity, and so the star continues to contract.
- High mass stars explode in a supernova, and leave behind either a neutron star or a black hole, depending on their size, whilst low mass stars become white dwarfs which gradually cool and fade away, and leave behind a planetary nebula.

2 A *[1 mark]*

Page 35 — Spectra from Stars

1 a) $d \sin \theta = n\lambda$ so $\lambda = d \sin \theta / n = (8.3 \times 10^{-7}) \sin 30.0 / 1$
$= 4.15 \times 10^{-7}$ m (to 3 s.f.) *[1 mark]*

b) The gases around the Sun absorb photons to move their electrons to higher energy levels *[1 mark]*. They can only absorb photons with the same energy as the energy needed for transitions between electron energy levels, hence only photons with certain wavelengths are absorbed *[1 mark]*.

c) $\Delta E = hc / \lambda = (6.63 \times 10^{-34} \times 3.00 \times 10^8) / 4.15 \times 10^{-7}$
$= 4.792... \times 10^{-19} = 4.79 \times 10^{-19}$ J (to 3 s.f.) *[1 mark]*
Which is also equal to 3.00 eV (to 3 s.f.) — either answer is acceptable.

d) $\lambda_{max} \propto \frac{1}{T}$, so $T\lambda_{max} =$ constant.
This means $T_{(Sun)}\lambda_{max (Sun)} = T_{(Rigel)}\lambda_{max (Rigel)}$
so $T_{(Sun)} = \frac{T_{(Rigel)} \lambda_{max (Rigel)}}{\lambda_{max (Sun)}}$ *[1 mark]* $= \frac{12\,000 \times 240 \times 10^{-9}}{490 \times 10^{-9}}$
$= 5877.55... = 5900$ K (to 2 s.f.) *[1 mark]*

e) $L = 4\pi r^2 \sigma T^4$
$= 4\pi \times (1.4 \times 10^9 \div 2)^2 \times 5.67 \times 10^{-8} \times 5877.55...^4$
$= 4.2 \times 10^{26}$ W (to 2 s.f.) *[1 mark]*

Page 37 — The Big Bang Theory

1 a) $\frac{\Delta\lambda}{\lambda} \approx \frac{v}{c}$ so $v \approx c\frac{\Delta\lambda}{\lambda} \approx 3.00 \times 10^8 \times \frac{890 \times 10^{-9} - 650 \times 10^{-9}}{650 \times 10^{-9}}$
$= 1.107... \times 10^8$
$= 1.1 \times 10^8$ ms^{-1} (to 2 s.f.) *[1 mark]*
away from us *[1 mark]*
You can tell the galaxy is moving away from us as the wavelength of the spectral line has increased (it has been red shifted).

b) $v = H_0 d$ so $d = v / H_0 = 1.107... \times 10^8 / 2.4 \times 10^{-18}$
$= 4.615... \times 10^{25}$ m *[1 mark]*
$4.615... \times 10^{25} / 9.5 \times 10^{15} = 4.9 \times 10^9$ ly (to 2 s.f.) *[1 mark]*

2 The light from other galaxies, apart from those closest to us, is red shifted, and the further away the galaxy, the greater the red shift. This shows that the galaxies are moving away from us, and the further away the are, the faster they are moving *[1 mark]*, which implies that the universe is expanding *[1 mark]*. If the universe is expanding, then in the past it must have been smaller, and if this logic is carried back to the beginning of the universe ($t = 0$) this suggests that all the matter in the universe existed in a single point *[1 mark]*.

Page 39 — The Evolution of the Universe

1 a) $H_0 = v / d = 50$ kms^{-1} / 1 Mpc^{-1}.
50 kms^{-1} $= 50 \times 10^3$ ms^{-1} and 1 Mpc $= 3.1 \times 10^{22}$ m
So, $H_0 = 50 \times 10^3$ ms^{-1} $\div 3.1 \times 10^{22}$ m $= 1.61... \times 10^{-18}$ s^{-1}
$= 1.6 \times 10^{-18}$ s^{-1} to (2 s.f.) *[1 mark for the correct value, 1 mark for the correct unit]*

b) $t = H_0^{-1}$ so $t = 1 / 1.61... \times 10^{-18} = 6.2 \times 10^{17}$ s *[1 mark]*
$6.2 \times 10^{17} \div (3.16 \times 10^7) = 1.962... \times 10^{10}$
$= 20$ billion years (to 2 s.f.) *[1 mark]*
So the observable universe has a radius of **20 billion light-years**. *[1 mark]*

2 E.g. the mass of clusters of galaxies as calculated from their velocities is greater than their mass as calculated from their luminosity *[1 mark]*, and stars at the edges of galaxies move faster than they should given the measurable mass and distribution of the stars within them *[1 mark]*. Both of these observations imply that there are extra sources of mass in the universe that we can't see *[1 mark]*. It is thought that this dark matter cannot all be made up of ordinary matter, as this would require more protons and neutrons to exist in the universe than is compatible with our current understanding of the Big Bang *[1 mark]*.

Module 6: Section 1 — Capacitors

Page 41 — Capacitors

1 Capacitance is the gradient of the Q-V graph.
$C = \frac{Q}{V} = \frac{660 \times 10^{-6}}{3}$ *[1 mark]* $= 220 \ \mu$F *[1 mark]*
Charge stored is the area under the I-t graph.
$\Delta Q = I\Delta t = 15 \times 10^{-3} \times 66$ *[1 mark]* $= 990$ mC *[1 mark]*

2 a) In series:
$\frac{1}{C_{total}} = \frac{1}{C_1} + \frac{1}{C_2} = \frac{1}{12 \times 10^{-12}} + \frac{1}{7 \times 10^{-12}} = 2.26... \times 10^{11}$
$C_{total} = \frac{1}{2.26... \times 10^{11}} = 4.42... \times 10^{-12}$ *[1 mark]*
$Q = CV = 4.42... \times 10^{-12} \times 12 = 5.305... \times 10^{-11}$
$= 5.3 \times 10^{-11}$ C (to 2 s.f.) *[1 mark]*

b) In parallel, $C_{total} = C_1 + C_2 = 12$ pF $+ 7.0$ pF $= 19$ pF *[1 mark]*
$Q = CV = 19 \times 10^{-12} \times 12 = 2.28 \times 10^{-10}$
$= 2.3 \times 10^{-10}$ C (to 2 s.f.) *[1 mark]*

Page 42 — Energy Stored by Capacitors

1 $W = \frac{1}{2}QV = \frac{1}{2} \times (0.6 \times 10^{-9}) \times 12 = 3.6 \times 10^{-9}$ J *[1 mark]*

2 $W = \frac{1}{2}CV^2$ so $C = \frac{2W}{V^2} = \frac{2 \times (2.5 \times 10^{-10})}{5^2} = 2 \times 10^{-11}$ F *[1 mark]*

Answers

Page 45 — Charging and Discharging

1 a) The charge falls to 37% after CR seconds *[1 mark]*
   so $t = 1000 \times 250 \times 10^{-6} = \textbf{0.25 s}$ *[1 mark]*

   b) $Q = Q_0 e^{\frac{-t}{CR}}$, so after 0.7 seconds: $Q = Q_0 e^{\frac{-0.7}{0.25}}$
      $= Q_0 \times 0.06$ (to 1 s.f.) *[1 mark]*
      So there is **6%** of the initial charge left on the
      capacitor after 0.7 seconds *[1 mark]*.

   c) i) The total charge stored will double (as $Q = CV$) *[1 mark]*.
      ii) None (the capacitance is fixed — the charge increases as the
          voltage increases, so $C = Q/V$ is constant) *[1 mark]*.
      iii) None (only capacitance and resistance can affect charging
          time) *[1 mark]*.

Module 6: Section 2 — Electric Fields

Page 47 — Electric Fields

1
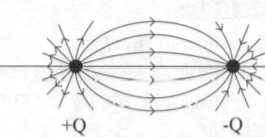
+Q   -Q

Recognisable pattern around the charges (not just in between)
[1 mark], lines equally spaced around the charges and joined
to the charges, and general symmetry of the diagram *[1 mark]*,
arrows along field lines between the charges with arrows pointing
away from the positive and towards the negative charge *[1 mark]*.

2 $E = \dfrac{Q}{4\pi\varepsilon_0 r^2}$
  $E = \dfrac{-1.60 \times 10^{-19}}{4\pi \times 8.85 \times 10^{-12} \times (1.75 \times 10^{-10})^2}$ *[1 mark]*
  $= -4.697... \times 10^{10} = \textbf{−4.70} \times \textbf{10}^{\textbf{10}} \textbf{ NC}^{\textbf{−1}}$ **(to 3 s.f.)** *[1 mark]*

3 $E = V/d = 1500/(4.5 \times 10^{-3}) = 3.33... \times 10^5$ Vm^{-1}
  $= \textbf{3.3} \times \textbf{10}^{\textbf{5}} \textbf{ Vm}^{\textbf{−1}}$ **(to 2 s.f.)** *[1 mark]*
  The field is perpendicular to the plates. *[1 mark]*

4 $A = 5.0 \times 10^{-3} \times 5.0 \times 10^{-3} = 2.5 \times 10^{-5}$ m^2 *[1 mark]*
  $\varepsilon = \varepsilon_r\varepsilon_0 = 4.1 \times 8.85 \times 10^{-12} = 3.6285 \times 10^{-11}$ *[1 mark]*
  $C = \dfrac{\varepsilon A}{d} = \dfrac{3.6285 \times 10^{-11} \times 2.5 \times 10^{-5}}{2 \times 10^{-3}}$
  $C = 4.535... \times 10^{-13} = \textbf{4.5} \times \textbf{10}^{\textbf{−13}} \textbf{ F}$ **(to 2 s.f.)** *[1 mark]*

Page 49 — Electric Potential

1 a) $V = \dfrac{Q}{4\pi\varepsilon_0 r} = \dfrac{-1.60 \times 10^{-19}}{4\pi \times 8.85 \times 10^{-12} \times 0.00100}$ *[1 mark]*
      $= -1.438... \times 10^{-6} = \textbf{−1.44} \times \textbf{10}^{\textbf{−6}} \textbf{ V}$ **(to 3 s.f.)** *[1 mark]*

   b) $E = Vq = -1.438... \times 10^{-6} \times 1.60 \times 10^{-19} = -2.301... \times 10^{-25}$
      $= \textbf{−2.30} \times \textbf{10}^{\textbf{−25}} \textbf{ J}$ **(to 3 s.f.)** *[1 mark]*

   c) $V = \dfrac{Q}{4\pi\varepsilon_0 r}$ so $r = \dfrac{Q}{4\pi\varepsilon_0 V}$
      $r = \dfrac{-1.60 \times 10^{-19}}{4\pi \times 8.85 \times 10^{-12} \times -1.0 \times 10^{-6}}$ *[1 mark]*
      $r = 1.4386... \times 10^{-3}$ m $= \textbf{1.4} \times \textbf{10}^{\textbf{−3}} \textbf{ m}$ **(to 2 s.f.)** *[1 mark]*

2 diameter $= 2r$ so $r = 5.00$ cm
  $C = 4\pi\varepsilon_0 r = 4 \times \pi \times 8.85 \times 10^{-12} \times 0.0500 = 5.560... \times 10^{-12}$
  $= \textbf{5.56} \times \textbf{10}^{\textbf{−12}} \textbf{ F}$ **(to 3 s.f.)** *[1 mark]*

3 Similarities — Any two from: gravitational field strength, g, is
  force per unit mass and electric field strength, E, is force per unit
  positive charge. Gravitational potential, V, is potential energy per
  unit mass and electric potential, V, is potential energy per unit
  charge. Both are zero at infinity. The force between two point
  masses is an inverse square law, and so is the force between two
  point charges. The field lines for a point mass and the field lines
  for a negative point charge are the same.
  Differences — Any one from: gravitational forces are always
  attractive, whereas electric forces can be attractive or repulsive.
  The size of an electric force depends on the medium between the
  charges, e.g. plastic or air. For gravitational forces, this makes no
  difference. Objects can be shielded from electric fields, but not
  from gravitational fields. *[1 mark for each correct statement]*

Module 6: Section 3 — Electromagnetism

Page 51 — Magnetic Fields

1 a) $F = BIl = 2.00 \times 10^{-5} \times 3.00 \times 0.0400 = \textbf{2.40} \times \textbf{10}^{\textbf{−6}} \textbf{ N}$ *[1 mark]*
   b) $F = BIl\sin\theta = 2.40 \times 10^{-6} \times \sin(30.0) = \textbf{1.20} \times \textbf{10}^{\textbf{−6}}$ *[1 mark]*

Page 53 — Charged Particles in Magnetic Fields

1 a) $F = BQv = 0.770 \times 1.60 \times 10^{-19} \times 5.00 \times 10^6$ *[1 mark]*
      $= \textbf{6.16} \times \textbf{10}^{\textbf{−13}} \textbf{ N}$ *[1 mark]*

   b) The force acting on the electron is always at right angles to its
      velocity and the speed of the electron is constant. This is the
      condition for circular motion. *[1 mark]*

2 Electromagnetic force = centripetal force *[1 mark]*
  $BQv = \dfrac{mv^2}{r}$, so $r = \dfrac{mv}{BQ}$ *[1 mark]*
  $= \dfrac{(9.11 \times 10^{-31}) \times (2.30 \times 10^7)}{(0.600 \times 10^{-3}) \times (1.60 \times 10^{-19})}$
  $= 0.21826... = \textbf{0.218 m}$ **(to 3 s.f.)** *[1 mark]*

3 $r = \dfrac{mv}{BQ}$, which rearranges to give $B = \dfrac{mv}{rQ}$ *[1 mark]*
  For the Cl-35 ions and the Cl-37 ions, v, r and Q are all constant,
  so $\dfrac{B}{m} = $ constant.
  Find the constant when $B = 0.200$ T, $m = 35$ u
  $0.200 \div 35 = 5.714... \times 10^{-3}$ *[1 mark]*
  Now use this value to find B when $m = 37$ u
  $B = 37 \times 5.714... \times 10^{-3} = 0.2114... = \textbf{0.21 T}$ **(to 2 s.f.)** *[1 mark]*
  The units of the atomic masses in this question don't matter — you're just
  interested in the ratio of B to m to get the constant.

Page 55 — Electromagnetic Induction

1 a) $\phi = BA = (2.00 \times 10^{-3}) \times 0.230 = \textbf{4.60} \times \textbf{10}^{\textbf{−4}} \textbf{ Wb}$ *[1 mark]*
   b) Flux linkage $= BAN = (2.00 \times 10^{-3}) \times 0.230 \times 151 = 0.06946$
      $= \textbf{0.0695 Wb}$ **(to 3 s.f.)** *[1 mark]*
   c) $\varepsilon = -\dfrac{\Delta(N\phi)}{\Delta t} = -\dfrac{\Delta(NBA)}{\Delta t} = -\dfrac{NA\Delta B}{\Delta t}$ *[1 mark]*
      $= -\dfrac{151 \times 0.230 \times (1.50 \times 10^{-3} - 2.00 \times 10^{-3})}{2.5}$ *[1 mark]*
      $= 6.946 \times 10^{-3} = \textbf{6.95} \times \textbf{10}^{\textbf{−3}} \textbf{V}$ **(to 3 s.f.)** *[1 mark]*

2 a) Flux linkage $= BAN = 0.92 \times 0.010 \times 550 = \textbf{5.06 Wb}$ *[1 mark]*
   b) Flux linkage after movement
      $= BAN \cos\theta$
      $= 550 \times 0.92 \times 0.010 \times \cos 90° = \textbf{0 Wb}$ *[1 mark]*
      $\varepsilon = -\dfrac{\Delta(N\phi)}{\Delta t} = -\dfrac{0 - 5.06}{0.5} = 10.12 = \textbf{10 V}$ **(to 2 s.f.)** *[1 mark]*

3
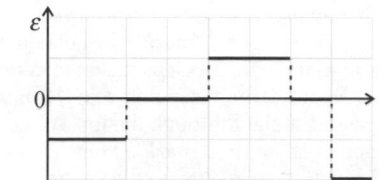

Step graph *[1 mark]* with the first and fifth steps negative and third
step positive *[1 mark]* and the last step twice as negative as the
others *[1 mark]*.

Page 57 — Electromagnetic Induction

1 a) Distance travelled by plane, $s = v\Delta t$.
      Wingspan $=$ length l, so area of flux cut $A = lv\Delta t$.
      So total magnetic flux cut $\phi = BA = Blv\Delta t$. *[1 mark]*
      E.m.f. $\varepsilon = -\dfrac{\Delta(N\phi)}{\Delta t} = -\dfrac{\Delta\phi}{\Delta t}$ (since $N = 1$), so
      $\varepsilon = -\dfrac{Blv\Delta t}{\Delta t} = -Blv$ *[1 mark]*
      $= -6.00 \times 10^{-5} \times 33.9 \times 148 = 0.301032$
      $= \textbf{−0.301 V}$ **(to 3 s.f.)** *[1 mark]*

b)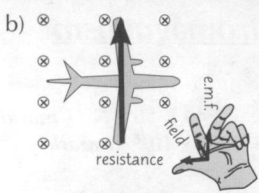

[1 mark]

Although there's no induced current, the direction that the current would be induced in if the plane were part of a complete circuit tells you the direction of the e.m.f..

2 a) $\varepsilon = -\frac{\Delta(N\phi)}{\Delta t} = -\frac{\Delta(BAN)}{\Delta t} = -\frac{AN\Delta B}{\Delta t}$ *[1 mark]*

$= -\frac{0.030 \times 75 \times ((150 \times 10^{-3}) - 0)}{7.5} = -\textbf{0.045 V} \textit{[1 mark]}$

b) When viewed from the south pole (on the right), the current will be clockwise *[1 mark]*. Lenz's law says that the e.m.f. induced in a coil will always be in such a direction as to oppose the change that caused it. The magnetic field due to the current induced in the coil must act from right to left to create a field that opposes the strengthening field, so by the right hand rule the current will be clockwise *[1 mark]*.

Page 59 — Uses of Electromagnetic Induction

1 a) i) $\frac{n_s}{n_p} = \frac{V_s}{V_p}$ so, $n_s = \frac{V_s \times n_p}{V_p} = \frac{45.0 \times 158}{9.30} = 764.51...$
$= \textbf{765 turns} \textit{[1 mark]}$

ii) $\frac{n_s}{n_p} = \frac{V_s}{V_p}$, so $V_s = V_p \times \frac{n_s}{n_p} = 9.30 \times \frac{90}{158}$
$= 5.297... = \textbf{5.30 V (to 3 s.f.)} \textit{[1 mark]}$

b) $\frac{I_s}{I_p} = \frac{V_p}{V_s}$ so, $I_s = I_p \times \frac{V_p}{V_s} = \frac{9.30 \times 1.50}{5.297...} = 2.6333...$
$= \textbf{2.63 A (to 3 s.f.)} \textit{[1 mark]}$

2 a) power transmitted = power received + power wasted *[1 mark]*
power transmitted = $943\,000 + I^2 \times R = 943\,000 + 15.6^2 \times 132$
$= 975\,123.52 = \textbf{975 kW (to 3 s.f.)} \textit{[1 mark]}$

b) Transformers are used to reduce the current (and increase the voltage) of electricity generated by power stations prior to transmitting it over the national grid *[1 mark]*. Transmitting electricity using a low current significantly reduces power lost during transmission because power lost is proportional to the current squared ($P = I^2R$) *[1 mark]*.

Module 6: Section 4 — Nuclear and Particle Physics

Page 61 — Atomic Structure

1 a) The nuclear model states that an atom consists of a positive nucleus containing protons and neutrons *[1 mark]*, surrounded by orbiting negative electrons *[1 mark]*. The nucleus makes up a tiny proportion of the volume of an atom, but most of its mass *[1 mark]*.

b) E.g. Most alpha particles passed straight through the foil, so there must be a lot of empty space in an atom *[1 mark]*. Some alpha particles were deflected through large angles, so the centre of the atom must have a large positive charge to repel them — the nucleus *[1 mark]*. Very few particles were deflected by more than 90 degrees, so the nucleus must be tiny *[1 mark]*.

2 Proton number = 57, so there are **57 protons** and **57 electrons**.
Nucleon number = no. of protons + no. of neutrons = 139
so no. of neutrons = 139 − 57 = **82 neutrons**
[2 marks for all correct, 1 mark for two correct]

Page 64 — The Nucleus

1 a) $R = r_0 A^{1/3} = 1.4 \times 10^{-15} \times 16^{1/3} = \textbf{3.5} \times \textbf{10}^{-15} \textbf{ m (to 2 s.f.)} \textit{[1 mark]}$

b) Nuclear radius is proportional to the cube root of A, so
$R \propto A^{1/3}$, so $\frac{R_{iodine}}{R_{nitrogen}} = \frac{(A_{iodine})^{1/3}}{(A_{nitrogen})^{1/3}} = \left(\frac{127}{14}\right)^{1/3}$ *[1 mark]*
$= 2.08...$

So the radius of the iodine nucleus is approximately **2 times** the radius of the nitrogen nucleus *[1 mark]*.

2 $V = \frac{4}{3}\pi r^3 = \frac{4}{3}\pi(8.53 \times 10^{-15})^3 = 2.599... \times 10^{-42} \text{ m}^3$ *[1 mark]*
$\rho = \frac{m}{V} = (3.75 \times 10^{-25}) \div (2.599... \times 10^{-42})$
$= \textbf{1.44} \times \textbf{10}^{17} \textbf{ kg m}^{-3} \textbf{ (to 3 s.f.)} \textit{[1 mark]}$

3 The density of a gold nucleus is much larger than the density of a gold atom *[1 mark]*. This implies that the majority of a gold atom's mass is contained in the nucleus *[1 mark]*. As the nucleus is small compared to the size of the atom *[1 mark]* there must be a lot of empty space inside each atom *[1 mark]*.

4 a) The strong nuclear force must be repulsive at very small nucleon separations to prevent the nucleus being crushed to a point *[1 mark]*.

b) Beyond a few fm, the strong nuclear force is smaller than the electrostatic force *[1 mark]*. This means the protons in the nucleus would be forced apart. So a nucleus bigger than this would be unstable *[1 mark]*.

Page 65 — Classification of Particles

1 A proton, an electron and an antineutrino *[1 mark]*.
The electron and the antineutrino are leptons *[1 mark]*. Leptons are not affected by the strong nuclear force, so the decay can't be due to the strong nuclear force *[1 mark]*.

2 A neutrino / an antineutrino *[1 mark]*

Page 67 — Antiparticles

1 The creation of a particle of matter requires the creation of its antiparticle. In this case no antineutron has been produced *[1 mark]*.

2 $e^+ + e^- \rightarrow \gamma + \gamma$ *[1 mark]*.
This is called annihilation *[1 mark]*.

3 The energy of each particle is equal to $\Delta E = mc^2$ (assuming kinetic energy is negligeable)
When the proton and the antiproton annihilate, two photons are produced. So $2E_\gamma = 2mc^2$ or $E_\gamma = mc^2$.
$E_\gamma = hf$ and equating, $mc^2 = hf$,
so $f = \frac{mc^2}{h}$ *[1 mark]*
$= \frac{(1.673 \times 10^{-27})(3.00 \times 10^8)^2}{(6.63 \times 10^{-34})}$ *[1 mark]*
$= \textbf{2.27} \times \textbf{10}^{23} \textbf{ Hz (to 3 s.f.)} \textit{[1 mark]}$

Page 69 — Quarks

1 **C** *[1 mark]*

2 a) i) $n \rightarrow p + e^- + \bar{\nu}$ *[2 marks — 1 mark for $n \rightarrow p$ and 1 mark for the electron and antineutrino]*

ii) $d \rightarrow u + e^- + \bar{\nu}$ *[1 mark]*

b) A down quark has a charge of −1/3, so the total charge on the left hand side of the equation is −1/3 *[1 mark]*. An up quark has a charge of +2/3, an electron has a charge of −1 and an antineutrino has no charge, so the total charge on the right-hand side of the equation is −1/3 *[1 mark]*. The charge is the same on both sides of the equation, so charge is conserved *[1 mark]*.

Page 72 — Radioactive Decay

1 **5-6 marks:**
The answer gives a full description of an experiment to identify the type of radiation emitted by a source, including the results expected for alpha, beta and gamma emitters. The answer includes a discussion of correcting for background radiation, and the safety measures that should be taken when working with radioactive sources. The answer has a clear and logical structure.
3-4 marks:
The answer describes an experiment to identify the type of radiation emitted by a source, including the results expected for alpha, beta and gamma emitters, but may omit some details. There is a limited discussion of the safety measures that should be taken when working with radioactive sources. The answer has some structure.

Answers

1-2 marks:

1-2 marks:
There is some description of an experiment to identify the type of radiation emitted by a source, but the answer lacks detail. The answer has no clear structure.
0 marks:
No relevant information is given.
Here are some points your answer may include:

- Measure the background count for a fixed amount of time (e.g. at least 30 seconds) and divide by the time to get the count rate.
- Take at least three measurements and calculate an average background count rate.
- The background count rate should be subtracted from all of the results.
- Place the source in front of a Geiger-Müller tube attached to a Geiger-Müller counter, so that the counter records a high count rate.
- Insert different materials between the source and the tube, and record the count rate by measuring the count over fixed time interval e.g. 30 seconds.
- If the count rate drops significantly, then some of the radiation is being absorbed by the material. If it drops to zero after the background count rate has been subtracted, then all of the radiation is being absorbed.
- If the radiation is blocked by a piece of paper, the source is emitting alpha radiation.
- If the radiation is blocked by a thin (3 mm) sheet of aluminium, the source is a beta emitter.
- If a thick sheet of lead is needed to block the radiation, then the source is a gamma emitter.
- The radioactive source should only be handled using long-handled tongs and should not be pointed at anyone.
- The radioactive source should be kept in a lead-lined box when not in use.
- Repeat the experiment to confirm the results.

2 a) $^{226}_{88}\text{Ra} \rightarrow \, ^{222}_{86}\text{Rn} + \, ^{4}_{2}\alpha$ *[3 marks available — 1 mark for alpha particle, 1 mark each for proton and nucleon number of radon]*

b) $^{40}_{19}\text{K} \rightarrow \, ^{40}_{20}\text{Ca} + \, ^{0}_{-1}\beta + \, ^{0}_{0}\bar{\nu}$ *[3 marks available — 1 mark for beta particle and antineutrino, 1 mark each for proton and nucleon number of calcium]*

Page 75 — Exponential Law of Decay

1 a) Activity, A = measured activity – background activity
   = $750 - 50 = 700$ Bq *[1 mark]*
   $A = \lambda N$, so $\lambda = A/N = 700 \div 50\,000 = \mathbf{0.014}$ $\mathbf{s^{-1}}$ *[1 mark]*

b) $\lambda t_{1/2} = \ln 2$, so $t_{1/2} = (\ln 2)/\lambda = (\ln 2) \div 0.014$
   = **50 s (to 2 s.f.)** *[1 mark]*

c) $N = N_0 e^{-\lambda t} = 50\,000 \times e^{-0.014 \times 300} = \mathbf{750}$ **(to 2 s.f.)** *[1 mark]*

Page 77 — Binding Energy

1 a) There are 6 protons and 8 neutrons, so the mass of individual parts = $(6 \times 1.007276) + (8 \times 1.008665) = 14.112976$ u *[1 mark]*
   Mass of $^{14}_{6}\text{C}$ nucleus = 13.999948 u
   Mass defect = $14.112976 - 13.999948 = \mathbf{0.113028}$ **u** *[1 mark]*

b) $0.113028 \times 1.661 \times 10^{-27} = 1.87739... \times 10^{-28}$ kg *[1 mark]*
   $\Delta E = \Delta mc^2 = (1.87739... \times 10^{-28}) \times (3.00 \times 10^8)^2$
   = $1.68965... \times 10^{-11}$ J *[1 mark]*
   1 eV = 1.60×10^{-19} J, so energy = $1.68965... \times 10^{-11} / 1.60 \times 10^{-19}$
   = $1.056... \times 10^8$ eV
   = **106 MeV (to 3 s.f.)** *[1 mark]*

2 a) Fusion *[1 mark]*

b) There are two deuterium atoms before the reaction, each containing two nucleons, so:
   binding energy before reaction = $2 \times 2 \times 1.11 = 4.44$ MeV *[1 mark]*
   There is one helium atom after the reaction, containing three nucleons, and a free neutron with a binding energy of zero, so:
   binding energy after reaction = $(2.58 \times 3) + 0 = 7.74$ MeV *[1 mark]*
   Energy released = difference in binding energy = $7.74 - 4.44$
   = **3.30 MeV** *[1 mark]*

Page 79 — Nuclear Fission and Fusion

1 a) E.g. control rods limit the rate of fission by absorbing neutrons *[1 mark]*. The number of neutrons absorbed by the rods is controlled by varying the amount they are inserted into the reactor *[1 mark]*. A suitable material for the control rods is boron *[1 mark]*.

b) In an emergency shut-down, the control rods are released into the reactor *[1 mark]*. The control rods absorb the neutrons, and stop the reaction as quickly as possible *[1 mark]*.

2 Advantages: e.g., the reaction in a nuclear reactor doesn't produce carbon dioxide *[1 mark]*, it can produce a continuous supply of electricity, unlike some renewable sources *[1 mark]*.
   [1 mark for each advantage, maximum 2 marks]
   Disadvantages — any two of: e.g. it could be dangerous if the reactor gets out of control, as a runaway reaction could cause an explosion *[1 mark]* / nuclear fission produces radioactive waste which is dangerous if it escapes into the environment *[1 mark]* / nuclear power-plants are expensive to build and decommission *[1 mark]* / nuclear waste has a long half-life, so has to be managed for a long time *[1 mark]*.
   [1 mark for each disadvantage, maximum 2 marks]

Module 6: Section 5 — Medical Imaging

Page 81 — X-Ray Imaging

1 $I = I_0 e^{-\mu x} = 200 \times e^{-(27 \times 1.5)}$
   $= 5.15... \times 10^{-16} = \mathbf{5.2 \times 10^{-16}}$ **Wm^{-2} (to 2 s.f.)** *[1 mark]*

2 Equate the two equations for the energy of the photon
   $eV = \dfrac{hc}{\lambda}$ so $V \propto \dfrac{1}{\lambda}$
   If $\lambda \rightarrow \dfrac{\lambda}{3}$, then $V \propto \dfrac{3}{\lambda}$, so V increases by a factor of 3 *[1 mark]*.
   $V = 3 \times 40$ kV = **120 kV** *[1 mark]*

Page 83 — Medical Uses of Nuclear Radiation

1 E.g. the patient is injected with a medical tracer consisting of a gamma source/positron-emitter bound to a substance used by the body *[1 mark]*. After a period of time, the radiation emitted from different points in the patient's body is recorded using a gamma camera/PET scanner *[1 mark]*. A computer uses this information to form an image, which might show a tumour as an area of high metabolic activity *[1 mark]*. One advantage of this method is that a diagnosis can be made without the patient having to undergo surgery.
   A disadvantage is the use of ionising radiation, which can damage and even kill cells in a patient's body *[1 mark]*.

Page 85 — Ultrasound Imaging

1 $Z = \rho c$, $c = (1.63 \times 10^6)/(1.09 \times 10^3)$ *[1 mark]*
   $= 1495$ ms^{-1} = **1.50 kms^{-1} (to 3 s.f.)** *[1 mark]*

2 When no gel is used:
   $\dfrac{(Z_{tissue} - Z_{air})^2}{(Z_{tissue} + Z_{air})^2} = \dfrac{(1630 \times 10^3 - 0.430 \times 10^3)^2}{(1630 \times 10^3 + 0.430 \times 10^3)^2}$
   = 0.9989... *[1 mark]*
   So when no gel is used, 99.89...% is reflected, and so only 0.105...% enters the body *[1 mark]*.
   $\dfrac{(Z_{tissue} - Z_{gel})^2}{(Z_{tissue} + Z_{gel})^2} = \dfrac{(1630 \times 10^3 - 1500 \times 10^3)^2}{(1630 \times 10^3 + 1500 \times 10^3)^2}$
   = 0.00172... *[1 mark]*
   So when gel is used, 0.172...% is reflected, and so 99.82...% of the ultrasound enters the body *[1 mark]*.
   So the ratio is 99.82...% ÷ 0.105...%
   = **1000 : 1 (to the nearest power of 10)** *[1 mark]*.

Index

Index

Index